The Checkbooks Series

Electronics 2 Checkbook

Second Edition

S. A. Knight

Heinemann Professional Publishing

Heinemann Professional Publishing Ltd
Halley Court, Jordan Hill, Oxford OX2 8EJ

OXFORD LONDON MELBOURNE AUCKLAND

First published by Butterworth & Co. (Publishers) Ltd 1981
First published by Heinemann Professional Publishing Ltd 1988

British Library Cataloguing in Publication Data
Knight, S. A.
Electronics 2 Checkbook
(The Checkbook series).
1. Electric engineering – Problems,
exercises, etc.
I. Title II. Series
621.30246 TK145

ISBN 0 434 91082 1

Printed in Great Britain by Robert Hartnoll Ltd, Bodmin

Contents

Note to readers

Checkbooks are designed for students seeking technician or equivalent qualification through the courses of the Business and Technician Education Council (BTEC), the Scottish Technical Education Council, Australian Technical and Further Education Departments, East and West African Examinations Council and other comparable examining authorities in technical subjects.

Checkbooks use problems and worked examples to establish and exemplify the theory contained in technical syllabuses. *Checkbook* readers gain real understanding through seeing problems solved and through solving problems themselves. *Checkbooks* do not supplant fuller textbooks, but rather supplement them with an alternative emphasis and an ample provision of worked and unworked problems, essential data, short answer and multi-choice questions (with answers where possible).

Digital Techniques 2
Digital Techniques 3
Electrical Applications 2
Electrical and Electronic Principles 2
Electrical Principles 3
Electronics 2
Electronics 3
Engineering Instrumentation and Control 4
Engineering Science 2
Engineering Science 3
Manufacturing Technology 2
Manufacturing Technology 3
Mathematics 1
Mathematics 2
Mathematics 3
Mathematics 4
Mechanical Science 3
Microelectronic Systems 1
Microelectronic Systems 2
Microelectronic Systems 3
Physical Science 1
Workshop Processes and Materials 1

Preface

An opportunity has been taken to revise and update this book to bring it into line with the essential syllabus requirements of BTEC Unit U86/331, Electronics level II. New chapters have been introduced to cover the additional requirements of work on unipolar transistors, sequential logic systems, stabilised power supplies and Karnaugh mapping principles. Some adjustments and additions have also been made to the existing chapters where syllabus changes have made them necessary.

As before, each chapter contains the relevant theory and definitions in summarised form, together with any essential formulae. Additional information is provided by way of worked examples which, it is hoped, will also demonstrate the best way to answer examination questions. Conventional and multi-choice problems for self-working are also included.

S. A. Knight

1 Elementary theory of semiconductors

A. MAIN POINTS CONCERNED WITH ELEMENTARY THEORY OF SEMICONDUCTORS

1 (i) All matter exists in a solid, liquid or gaseous state. The smallest particle of any substance that retains the characteristics of that substance is called a **molecule**. Each molecule is built up from a number of chemical elements, the smallest particles of each element being known as **atoms**.

Atoms are believed to be made up of a positively charged core or nucleus about which one or more negatively charged particles called **electrons** rotate in planetary orbits. The charge on an electron is very small, about -1.6×10^{-19} coulomb and its mass is estimated to be 9.1×10^{-31} kg.

Normally an atom is electrically neutral, the effect of the negative charges carried by the rotating electrons being exactly balanced by the positive charge carried by the nucleus. The nucleus is itself made up of two other types of particle, **protons** and **neutrons**, though not necessarily equal in number. Only the proton carries a postive charge, the neutrons being without charge. Hence, since the entire atom is neutral, the charge on a proton is equal to the charge on an electron but is of opposite sign. The proton is about 1840 times as massive as an electron, however, so the nucleus constitutes almost the entire mass of the atom.

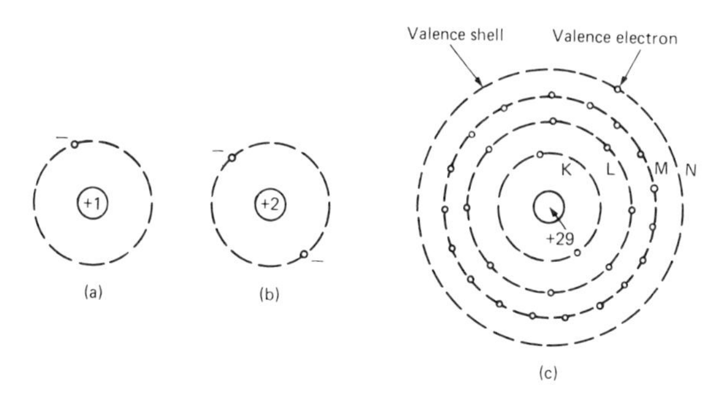

Fig 1(a) Hydrogen atom–a single proton in the nucleus with a single orbital electron
(b) Helium atom–two protons and two neutrons in the nucleus with two orbital electrons
(c) Copper atom–29 protons and 35 neutrons in the nucleus with 29 orbital electrons

(ii) The number of planetary electrons and the structure of the nucleus in an atom varies with the element. The lightest element, hydrogen, has only one proton as nucleus around which revolves a single electron. Next in the order is helium whose nucleus consists of two neutrons and two protons and about this revolves two electrons. Much further along the scale, an atom of copper consists of 29 protons and 35 neutrons in the nucleus, with 29 orbital electrons. These atoms are shown in *Fig 1*.

(iii) The revolving electrons are held in their respective orbital rings or **shells** by the attractive force of the nucleus. Most atoms have a number of shells and these are distinguished by assigning to them letters of the alphabet, starting at K for the innermost shell and proceeding through L, M and N to the outermost. The electrons making up the outermost shell are called **valence** electrons and these are least tightly bound to the nucleus. It is the valence electrons that play the active part in electrical conduction.

2 Solid materials are either **conductors** or **insulators** in their electrical properties. The behaviour of the valence electrons decides to which of these classes a particular material belongs. In insulating materials, i.e., mica, rubber and most plastics – the valence electrons are sufficiently tightly bound to the nucleus to remain in their orbits even when a large voltage is impressed across a piece of the material. Hence none of them become available to act as current carriers.

In a good conducting material – i.e., copper and aluminium – the valence electrons are only weakly bound to their atoms and many of them break free to drift within the atomic structure of the material. When a voltage is impressed across the material, these free electrons act as current carriers. Copper atoms have one valence electron as shown in *Fig 1* and this electron may become available as a charge carrier.

3 However, the distinction between insulators and conductors is not precisely defined and there are certain substances which are neither good insulators nor good conductors.

Into this category come the **semiconductors** which form the basis of all solid-state electronics. Semiconductors, notably germanium and silicon are crystalline materials in which the atoms are held together in a stable form by what is known as co-valent bonding.

Both germanium and silicon atoms have four valence electrons (they are **tetravalent** atoms). The structure of these elements is brought about by a sharing arrangement in which each atom has in effect, not four but eight valence electrons, its own four valence electrons being shared with those of an adjoining atom. A representation of this covalent bonding is shown in *Fig 2*, each band being a shared valence electron.

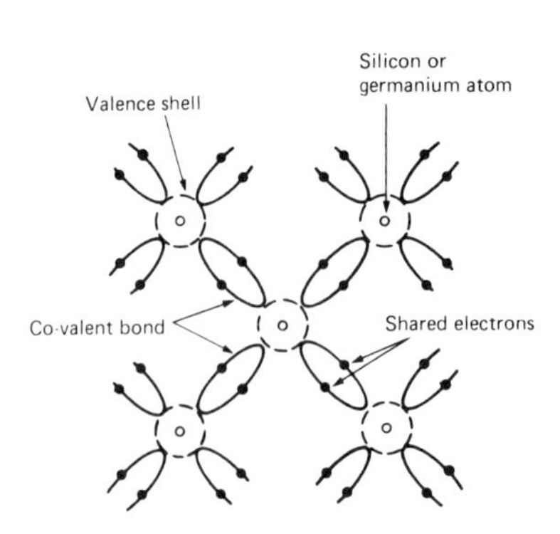

Fig 2

In this condition the atoms are in a very stable state and form throughout the material a geometrical arrangement which is known as a crystal lattice. Consequently, there are no free electrons available to act as charge carriers and the resulting crystal is an effective insulator. This situation is only true if two conditions are satisfied. Firstly, the crystal structure must be perfect in that all the covalent bonds are satisfied and, secondly, the temperature must be very low.

At room temperature, thermal vibration of the atoms breaks some of the covalent bonds and this, together with structural faults and impurities within the crystal provides free electrons which wander about among the atoms. The effect is accelerated as the temperature increases. Thus **thermally generated** electrons increase in numbers and turn the crystal from a very good insulator into a conductor, even if a relatively poor one.

4 Unlike those in copper (for example), electrons are not the only charge carriers produced in germanium or silicon. Where an electron breaks free, a vacancy or **hole** is left in the crystal structure. Since this hole has been formed by the removal of a negatively charged electron, the hole must behave as a positive charge.

If the material is connected to a voltage source, then the applied field attracts the free electrons towards the positive pole, whilst further free electrons flow in from the positive pole and travel through the semiconductor by moving from hole to hole.

This process can be looked on as electrons moving from negative to positive within the semiconductor (as well as in the external circuit wires) and holes moving from positive to negative within the semiconductor only. Both of these movements contribute to conduction and thus a current is maintained around the circuit (see *Fig 3*).

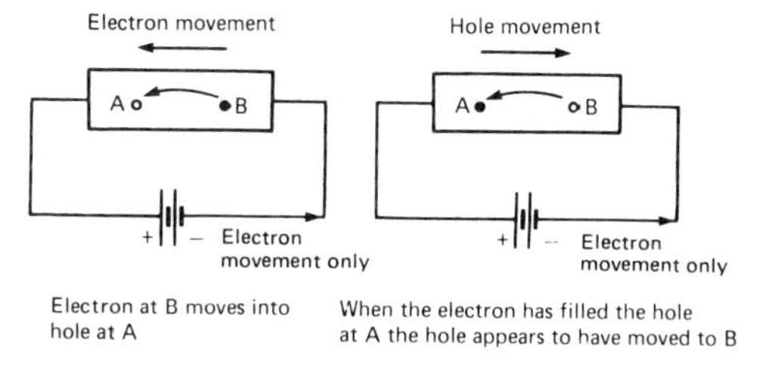

Fig 3

As the temperature is raised, more electron and hole pairs become available and the conductivity increases. The weak conductivity which results from such thermal effects is known as **intrinsic** conductivity.

5 Because of its dependence upon temperature, intrinsic conductivity is of no practical importance. The manufacture of useable semiconductor material involves changes in the conduction characteristics so that either electrons *or* holes become the dominant charge carriers. This is done by the addition of an impurity into the semiconductor material.

Certain other elements have atoms which are able to fit into the crystal lattice of germanium or silicon without seriously upsetting the regular geometric construction. If the valency of these added atoms is different from those in the semiconductor material itself, then conductivity is enormously increased.

Fig 4 shows what happens when the atoms of the impurity have five valence electrons. Four of the five valence electrons from each added atom go to satisfy the valence bonds with neighbouring semiconductor atoms, but the fifth is 'left over' to move about the crystal and act as a charge carrier.

An impurity of this type is called a **donor** since it donates electrons as negative charge carriers. The doped material is now referred to as *n*–type semiconductor and electrons are the majority carriers.

Fig 5 shows the effect of adding impurity atoms which have three valence electrons. As before, each semiconductor atom has four valence electrons but the impurity atom has now only three. Only three valence bonds with neighbouring atoms can therefore be satisfied by the added atoms, so that a hole appears in what would have been the fourth bond.

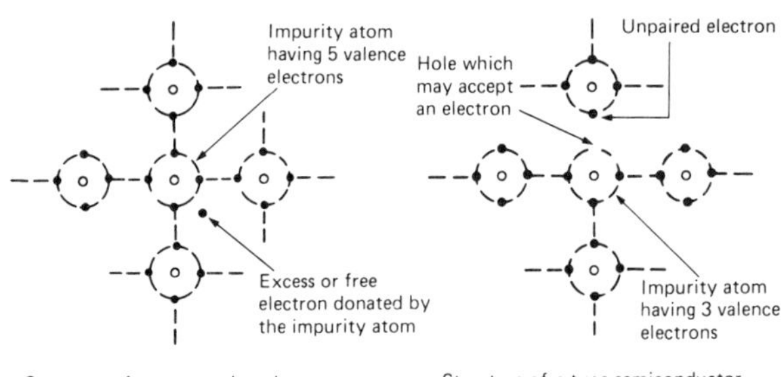

Structure of *n*-type semiconductor

Structure of *p*-type semiconductor

Fig 4

Fig 5

Such an impurity gives the semiconductor an abundance of holes. We now have *p*–type material and the positive holes are the majority carriers. This time the impurity atoms are called **acceptors** because they can accept electrons from the surrounding crystal structure.

6 The doping of semiconductor material to produce majority carriers and so increase the conductivity does not mean that the thermally generated hole-electron pairs is no longer occurring. In *n*–type material, for example, as well as the many free electrons contributed by the donor impurity, there are a relatively small number of holes present because of such thermal breaking of the co-valent bonds. Similarly, in *p*–type material, thermally generated electrons are present.

Such unwanted carriers are known as minority carriers. Under an impressed voltage minority carriers move in the opposite direction to majority carriers but their numbers depend upon the temperature and *not* upon the added impurity atoms.

When a semiconductor has been doped with a suitable impurity, it is referred to as **extrinsic** *p*– or *n*–type, and the conduction which takes place is extrinsic conduction.

B. WORKED PROBLEMS ON ELEMENTARY THEORY OF SEMICONDUCTORS

Problem 1 Compare the change in conductivity between a semiconductor material and a metal like a copper as the temperature is raised.

As the temperature of a semiconductor is raised, more covalent bonds are broken, more hole-electron pairs become available, and the conductivity increases. In a conductor, such as copper where there is an abundance of free electrons available even at a low temperatures, the conductivity depends upon the ability of these electrons to move through the material without colliding with the metal atoms.

As the temperature increases, the amplitude of vibration of the atoms due to the thermal energy increases so that they impede the movement of the charge carriers and the conductivity falls. Hence in semiconductor material resistance *falls* as temperature rises and in a metal conductor resistance *rises* as temperature rises. We say that semiconductors have a negative temperature coefficient.

Problem 2 Name the elements having three and five valence electrons respectively that may be used to dope semiconductor material.

Atoms that have three valence electrons are known as trivalent atoms. Trivalent impurity may be added by the introduction of the element boron, aluminium or indium. Atoms that have five valence electrons are pentavalent atoms. Examples of such impurity atoms are antimony, arsenic or phosphorus.

Problem 3 An atom of aluminium has a nucleus made up of 13 protons and 14 neutrons. It has three electron shells of which the inner contains 2 electrons. How many electrons are there in the middle shell?

Aluminium is trivalent so it has three electrons in the valence shell. As the atom is electrically neutral, there must be 13 electrons in the three shells, hence there must be $13 - 5 = 8$ electrons in the middle shell.

Problem 4 Sketch and briefly describe the make up of germanium and silicon atoms.

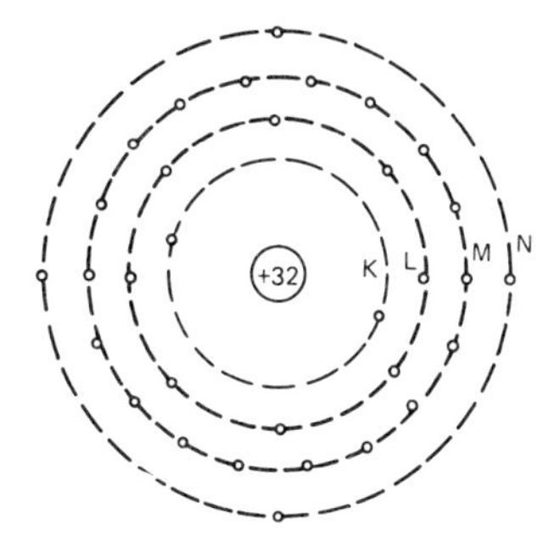

Fig 6(a) Germanium atom—a nucleus of 32 protons and 42 neutrons with 4 shells containing respectively 2, 8, 18 and 4 electrons

Germanium and silicon are the most extensively used semiconductors in the manufacture of transistors. Germanium is a greyish-white metallic element, made by reduction in a hydrogen or helium atmosphere of germanium dioxide. The dioxide is obtained as a component of the chimney soot from gasworks. The germanium atom is shown in *Fig 6(a)*; it has a nucleus of 32 protons and 42 neutrons with 4 orbital shells containing respectively 2, 8, 18 and 4 electrons.

Silicon is a non-metallic element, being second only to oxygen in its abundance in the earth's crust. It never occurs in nature in the free state, but in complex silicon compounds. Because of this it is more difficult to refine to a high degree of purity than is germanium and all the early solid-state devices were germanium based. The silicon atom is shown in *Fig 6(b)*. It has a nucleus of 14 protons and 14 neutrons with three orbital shells containing respectively 2, 8 and 4 electrons.

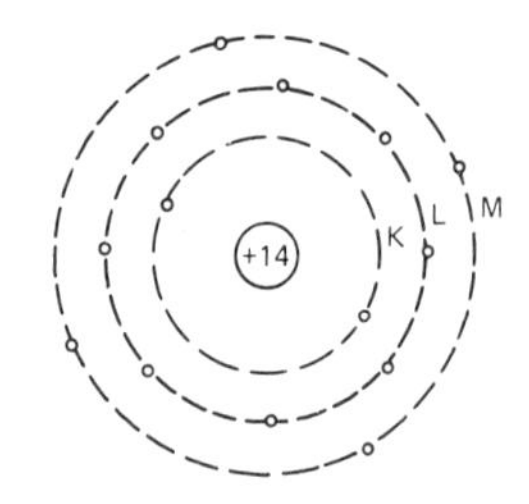

Fig 6(b) Silicon atom—a nucleus of 14 protons and 14 neutrons with 3 shells containing respectively 2, 8 and 4 electrons

Problem 5 If impurity semiconductors have an excess of electrons or holes as charge carriers, why are these charges not lost when the semiconductor is connected to earth?

Although, for example, there are free electrons in *n*–type semiconductor due to the addition of impurity atoms having five valence electrons, the crystal as a whole is electrically neutral as each impurity atom introduced is itself electrically neutral. This is true of any conductor; a length of copper wire, for example, although having an abundance of free electrons available as current carriers is not in any way negatively charged.

C. FURTHER PROBLEMS ON ELEMENTARY THEORY OF SEMICONDUCTORS

(a) SHORT ANSWER PROBLEMS (answers on page 132)

1 Atoms are made up from electrons, protons and with one exception, neutrons. Name the exception.

2 The K, L and M shells of a sodium atom contains 2, 8 and 1 electrons respectively. How many protons are there in the nucleus?

3 The phosphorus atom has three shells and its nucleus contains 15 protons. The K and L shells contain 2 and 8 electrons respectively. Would phosphorus impurity produce a p-type or an n-type semiconductor?

4 Fill in the blank spaces in the following table:

	Protons	K	L	M	N	shells
Aluminium	13	2		3	0	
Argon		2	8	8	0	
Copper	29	2	8		1	
Magnesium	12	2	8			

5 Complete the following statements:
   (a) The atomic nucleus is made up of . . . . and . . . .
   (b) In an intrinsic semiconductor there will always be . . . . number of holes and electrons.
   (c) Intrinsic semiconduction is that conduction which takes place in a crystal of pure silicon or germanium when all current carriers are provided by . . . . produced when . . . . energy breaks the covalent bonds.
   (d) The impurity atoms added to silicon to produce holes are known as . . . . atoms.
   (e) *n*- and *p*-type impurity semiconductors are known as . . . . semi-conductors.
   (f) Reducing the temperature causes the resistivity of semiconductors to . . . . and that of conductors to . . . .

6 Are the following true or false?
   (a) At 0°C pure silicon is a perfect insulator.
   (b) The conductivity of intrinsic germanium increases with temperature.
   (c) In extrinsic semiconductors, the majority carriers are determined by the number of impurity atoms present.
   (d) The majority carriers in extrinsic material cannot change with change in temperature.
   (e) Atoms of phosphorus are known as acceptor impurities.
   (f) In *p*-type material the majority carriers are holes.
   (g) If the temperature of an intrinsic semiconductor is increased, the number of hole-electron pairs increases.
   (h) *n*-type material is made by the addition of pentavalent material to an instrinsic semiconductor.
   (j) The charge on a hole is the same as the charge on an electron but of opposite sign.

7 Name three good conductors and three good insulators of electricity.

8 Name two semiconductor materials and compare their properties in relations to (a) a good conductor, (b) a good insulator.

9 Name a suitable doping element for obtaining (a) *n*-type semiconductor material; (b) *p*-type semiconductor material.

10 Name two trivalent materials used in the formation of *p*-type material.

(b) CONVENTIONAL PROBLEMS

1 Explain what is mean by (a) intrinsic; (b) extrinsic action in a semiconductor

2 The current in a copper conductor is 2 A. How many electrons pass a given point in 1 minute? (Charge of electron = 1.6×10^{-19} C)

3 In *Fig 7* the rectangle represents a piece of intrinsic semiconductor. Using arrows, show clearly the flow of charge carriers within the semiconductor and in the external circuit.

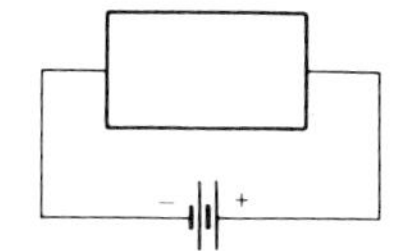

Fig 7

4 Explain the meaning of the following terms:

(a) electron shells; (b) co-valent bonds; (c) impurity atom;
(d) minority carriers; (d) intrinsic semiconductor; (f) extrinsic semiconductor;
(g) donor atoms; (h) acceptor atoms.

2 The *p-n* junction diode

A MAIN POINTS CONCERNED WITH THE *p–n* JUNCTION DIODE

1 (i) If a crystal of *n*-type semiconductor and a crystal of *p*-type semiconductor are joined, the combination is known as a *p-n* junction. Such a junction forms the basis of all diode and transistor action.

It is not possible to get the desired result simply by clamping two pieces of semiconductor crystal together because there is a discontinuity in the crystal structure at the line of contact. The crystal structure must be complete throughout the junction and *Fig 1* shows two possible ways (out of several) of achieving this result. Either the *n*- and *p*-regions are grown into pure semiconductor crystal by mixing the donor and acceptor impurities respectively into the crystal during its formation, diagram (a), so producing a single crystal which has *n*-type characteristics at one end and *p*-type characteristics at the other; or a junction is made by placing a small pellet of, say, acceptor impurity such as indium, on one face of a thin wafer of *n*-type material and then heating the assembly to alloy the impurity pellet into the body of the wafer. This the **alloy-junction** or diffused alloy form of construction, and diagram (b) illustrate the basic process.

(ii) Another form of construction is possible using a fine, pointed tungsten wire, known as the 'catswhisker', pressed into contact with a small wafer of *n*-type material. *Fig 2* shows one typical form of assembly; this is the **point-contact**

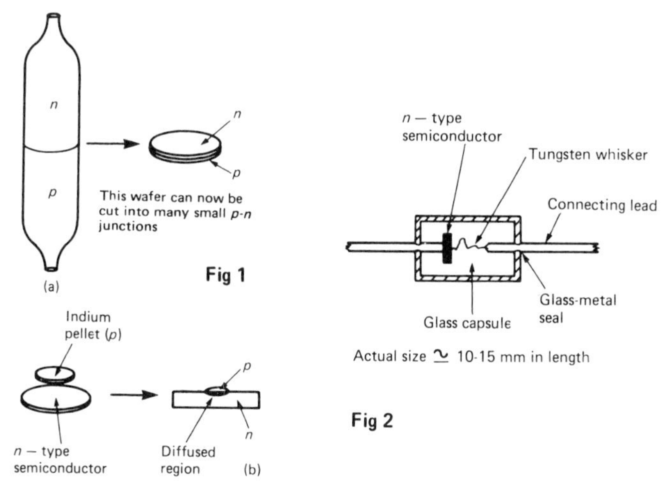

Fig 1

Fig 2

junction. After assembly, a high current pulse is passed momentarily across the junction of whisker and wafer. This current surge creates heat and drives a number of electrons away from the atoms in the region of the point contact, leaving holes and so converting a small volume of the wafer immediately under and around the point into *p*-type material. A *p-n* junction is so produced surrounding the metal point.

2 To understand the operation of a *p-n* junction as a practical semiconductor device, we must look at the way the free charge carriers, electrons and holes, behave in the two types of semiconductor when the junction is formed.

In *Fig 3*, the *p*-region has holes (open circles) and the *n*-region has electrons (filled circles) available as majority carriers. Notice that a few electrons are shown

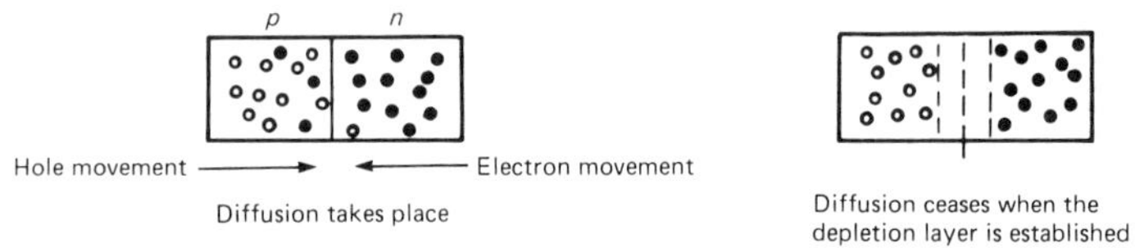

Fig 3

in the *p*-region and a few holes in the *n*-region, but in each case these minority carriers are far outnumbered by the majority carriers.

Holes, having a positive charge, move from the *p*-region on the left of the junction into the *n*-region on the right. At the same time, electrons having a negative charge, move from the *n*-region on the right of the junction into the *p*-region on the left. This initial movement of charges, which takes place as soon as the junction is formed, is known as **diffusion**.

The electrons and holes that have diffused across the junction in this way are soon lost in recombination. Hence a very thin region is established on each side of the junction line in which no free carriers are present. This region is called the **depletion layer** and it separates the charges on the two sides of the junction.

As soon as this separation is established, an electric field is developed across the junction and further diffusion is stopped. Since the *p*-side has gained electrons and the *n*-side has gained holes, the *p*-side will become negative with respect to the *n*-side and the field acts in such a direction that it tends to prevent more negative charges leaving the *n*-region and more positive charges from leaving the *p*-region.

The situation is then equivalent to a source of potential acting across the junction

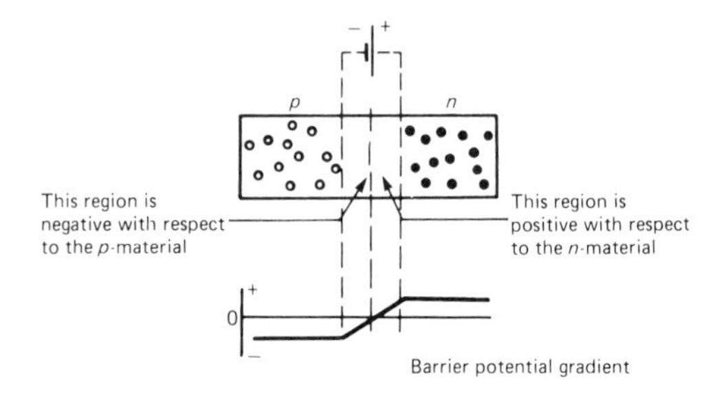

Fig 4

and represented by a hypothetical battery E connected as shown in *Fig 4*. Make a careful note of the polarity of this **barrier potential** as it is called. The graph drawn underneath the diagram is a simple representation of the variation in potential acting across the junction.

The minority carriers have now to be considered. Thermally produced hole-electron pairs will occur in the regions near the junction. The holes produced in the *n*-region and the electrons produced in the *p*-region will be minority carriers and will tend to be *assisted* across the junction by the same barrier potential which is opposing the movement of majority carriers. The movement of these minority carriers is equivalent to a coventional current flowing from *n* to *p*, that is, in the opposing direction to the recombination movement.

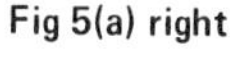

Fig 5(a) right

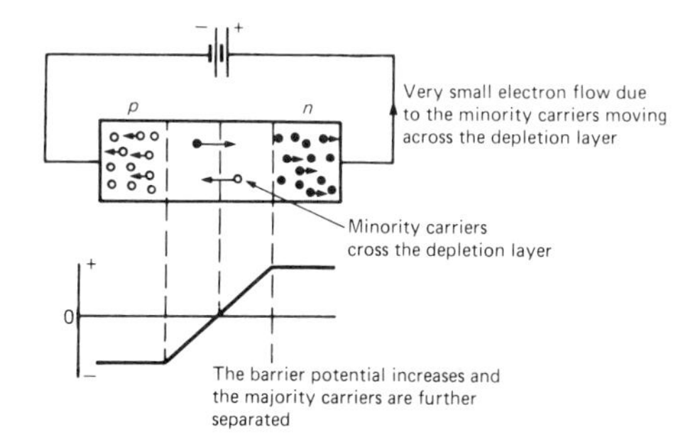

Fig 5(b) below

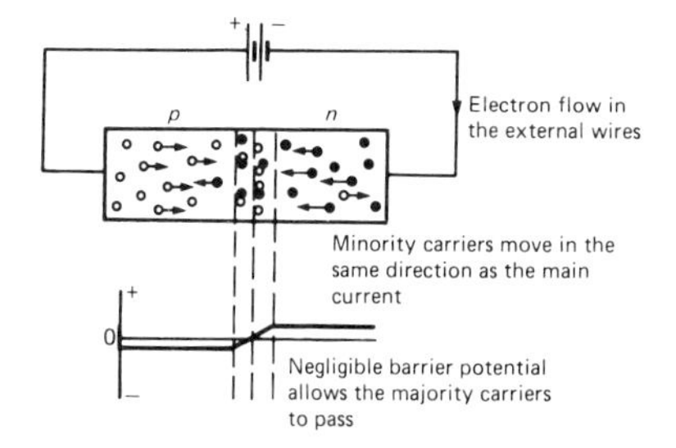

The actual barrier potential depends upon the densities of the carriers and the semiconductor material. It is about 0.2 – 0.3 V for germanium and 0.6 – 0.7 V for silicon.

3 Suppose now that a battery is connected externally to the *p-n* junction, acting in the direction shown in *Fig 5(a)*. Here the *p*-region is made negative and the *n*-region is made positive. Holes are attracted by the negative field and electrons by the positive field; in other words, the polarity of the external battery is such as to *assist* the junction barrier potential. Holes and electrons are both pulled away from the junction in the direction of the arrows.

This further separation of the majority carriers makes the junction resistance very high and the current flow around the external circuit is very low. It is not zero, however, as we might at first suspect, because the minority carriers on each side of the junction are attracted across the depletion layer by the barrier potential. The resulting flow of current by this movement of the minority carriers is known as the **reverse saturation** or **leakage** current and the *p-n* junction is said to be reverse-biased.

If the battery connections are changed over as shown in *Fig 2.5(b)* both holes and electrons are driven in the direction of the arrows *towards* the junction where recombination takes place. Since the junction potential barrier is now cancelled out, the junction resistance is very low and a large current flows around the circuit. The junction is now said to be forward-biased.

The current in the circuit consists of a flow of electrons in the external circuit and, considering only the majority carriers, electrons in the *n*-type region, electrons and holes across the junction, and holes in the *p*-type region.

4 If an alternating voltage is applied to the *p-n* junction as shown in *Fig 6* the circuit will alternately present a high resistance when the voltage assists the barrier

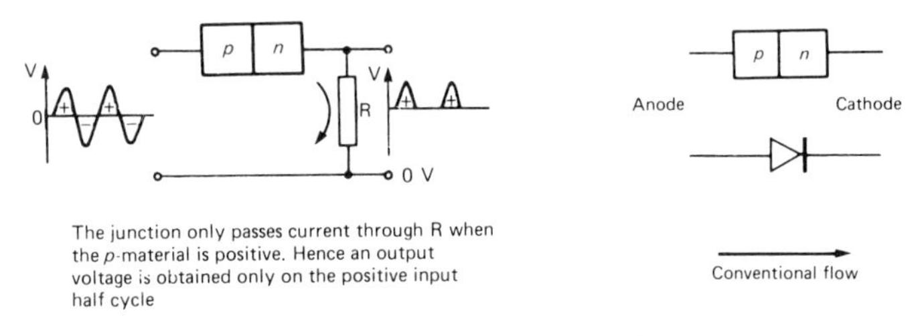

The junction only passes current through R when the *p*-material is positive. Hence an output voltage is obtained only on the positive input half cycle

Fig 6

Fig 7

potential and a low resistance when the voltage opposes the barrier potential.

A much larger current flows in the circuit during the input half-cycle when the resistance is low than during the other half-cycle when the resistance is high. The *p-n* junction can therefore be used as a rectifier element. The symbol for the *p-n* junction diode is shown in *Fig 7*. When you use this symbol, remember that the arrow points in the direction of *conventional* current flow. On this basis, the diode will conduct when the arrow is connected to the positive pole of the supply. The arrow then corresponds to the **anode** of the device and the bar to the **cathode**.

5 (i) The voltage-current characteristic of a *p-n* junction diode can be obtained from the circuit shown in *Fig 8*. The voltage applied to the diode is obtained from battery E and by using a centre-tapped potentiometer P, this voltage may be set to be either positive or negative at the diode anode relative to the cathode. Milliammeter A indicates the diode current.

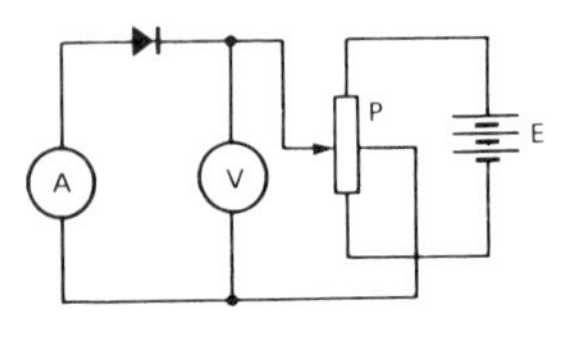

Fig 8

A typical characteristic showing both germanium and silicon diode curves is given in *Fig 9*. Such characteristics are known as **static** characteristics, the set-up being purely in terms of d.c. conditions.

In the case of germanium, the current through the diode in the forward direction (anode positive) rises rapidly beyond about 0.2 V, and at high positive voltages becomes substantially straight. When the voltage is reversed (anode negative) the current flowing is initially one or two microamperes,

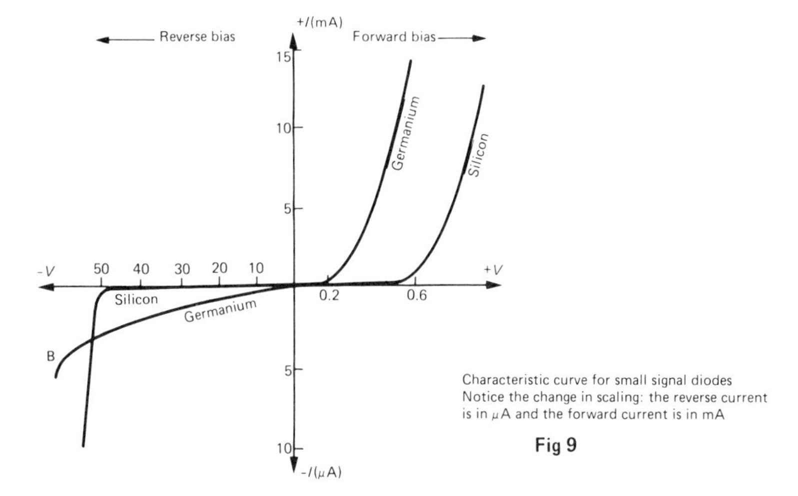

Characteristic curve for small signal diodes
Notice the change in scaling: the reverse current is in μA and the forward current is in mA

Fig 9

but increases fairly rapidly to what is known as the breakdown point at B, after which, unless steps are taken to prevent it, the current reaches a very large value and the diode may be damaged. Breakdown is due to the thermally generated electrons acquiring sufficient energy as they are accelerated by the field across the depletion layer to release further hole-electron pairs as they collide with the silicon or gemanium atoms. These additional carriers in turn generate still more carriers and the effect avalanches rapidly. Breakdown can occur at a reverse voltage as low as 5 V and as high as 1000 V or more, depending upon the form of construction and the doping levels of the diode.

Turning to the silicon diode, the current in the forward direction is similar in shape to that of germanium but it does not become appreciable until about 0.5–0.6 V is applied. The forward resistance of a silicon diode is clearly greater than that of a germanium diode for a given forward voltage.

The silicon reverse current remains very small, a matter of a few picoamperes, until the breakdown point is reached when there is a sudden increase, relative to germanium, for a very small further increase in the reverse voltage.

The forward or reverse resistance of either diode can be found for any point on the graph simply as the ratio V/I at that particular point.

(ii) It may seem that the best design procedure for any circuits containing semiconductor diodes would be to ensure that the reverse voltage could never exceed the breakdown voltage. This is true for diodes used as rectifiers, but there are other applications which actually make use of the reverse breakdown condition.

A diode which is designed to operate in the breakdown region is called a **zener diode**. These diodes are connected into a circuit in the reverse direction, that is, the anode is connected to the supply negative terminal and the cathode to the positive terminal. Hence breakdown occurs as soon as the applied voltage reaches the appropriate level. The voltage-current characteristic of a zenor diode is shown in *Fig. 10*. This shows that once breakdown has occurred the voltage across

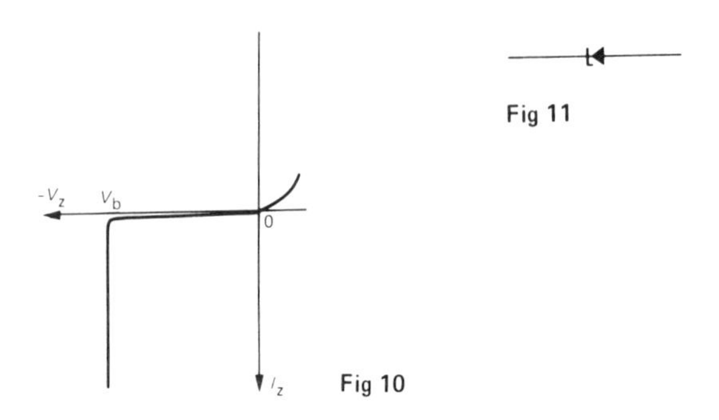

Fig 11

Fig 10

the diode remains substantially constant at the level V_b irrespective of wide variations in the current through it.

Provided the current is not allowed to become destructively great, the diode can be used for the special purpose of voltage stabilisation. The symbol for a zener diode is given in *Fig 11*.

B. WORKED PROBLEMS ON *p-n* JUNCTION DIODES

Problem 1. What effect have the minority carriers when the *p-n* junction is forward-biased?

When the junction is forward biased, the minority carriers simply move along with the majority carriers and do nothing more than make a very small contribution to the relatively large forward current which flows in the circuit.

Problem 2. Mention briefly the ways in which the fabrication and application of a point-contact diode differs from that of a diffused alloy junction diode.

In the point-contact diode, the *p*-type material is formed *after* the assembly of the device; in the junction diode the *p*-type material is formed *before* assembly. Because of the very small area of contact in the point-contact diode, the forward current is generally very much smaller than that of a junction type diode for a given applied voltage.

The fine wire of the catswhisker also reduces the power handling capabilities of the point-contact diode. Its internal capacitance is, however, much smaller than that of a junction diode and it is therefore much used for high-frequency applications.

Problem 3. What effect does temperature variation have on the leakage current in both silicon and germanium junctions?

When the temperature is very low, the production of hole-electron pairs by breaking of the co-valent bonds is negligibly small, hence there are relatively few minority carriers present and the reverse current is practically zero. As the temperature is raised, more and more minority carriers are generated and the leakage current increases.

Working from about 20°C each increase of 10°C very roughly doubles the rate of generation of minority carriers for germanium, or of 5°C for silicon. This might make it appear that germanium is the better material to use where high ambient temperatures are likely to be experienced, but this is not so.

Although the rate of increase is greater for silicon, its actual value at room temperature is considerably smaller than that of germanium (refer back to *Fig 9*), so silicon is used where high ambient and working temperatures are expected.

Problem 4. The leakage current of a certain germanium diode is 4 μA at 20°C. What orders of leakage would you expect at 70°C?

We have noted from *Problem 3* above that, for germanium, leakage current doubles approximately for very 10°C rise in temperature. From 20°C to 70°C there is a 50°C rise, or 5 x 10°C increases. Hence the current at 70°C will be about
$4 \times 2^5 = 128\ \mu A$

Problem 5. The two diodes shown in *Fig 12* can be assumed to have a forward resistance of 5 Ω and an infinite reverse resistance. Calculate the currents flowing in each branch of the circuit (a) when the battery is connected as shown, (b) when the battery is reversed.

(a) With the battery connected as shown, only diode D_1 will conduct. Hence the circuit reduces to 50 Ω in parallel with (25 + 5) = 30 Ω

The current in the 50 Ω resistor will be 100/50 = 2 A
The current in diode D_1 will be 100/30 = 3.33 A

(b) With the battery reversed diode D_1 will cut off and D_2 will conduct. Hence the circuit reduces to 50 Ω in parallel with (40 + 5) = 45 Ω

The current in the 50 Ω resistor will be unaffected and will remain at 2 A
The current in diode D_2 will be 100/45 = 2.22 A

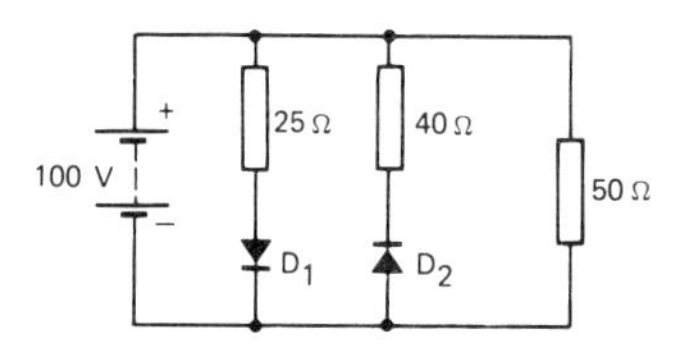

Fig 12

Problem 6. A diode has the following forward characteristics:

Current (mA)	0	0.9	4.0	9.8	18.2	30.0	48.0
Voltage (V)	0	0.5	1.0	1.5	2.0	2.5	3.0

The diode is connected in series with a 50 Ω resistor. Draw the voltage-current characteristic for the diode alone and on the same axes draw the voltage-current characteristic for the complete circuit. What current will flow if the applied voltage is 4.5 V?

The diode characteristic is plotted from the given table and is shown in solid line on the axes of *Fig 13*.

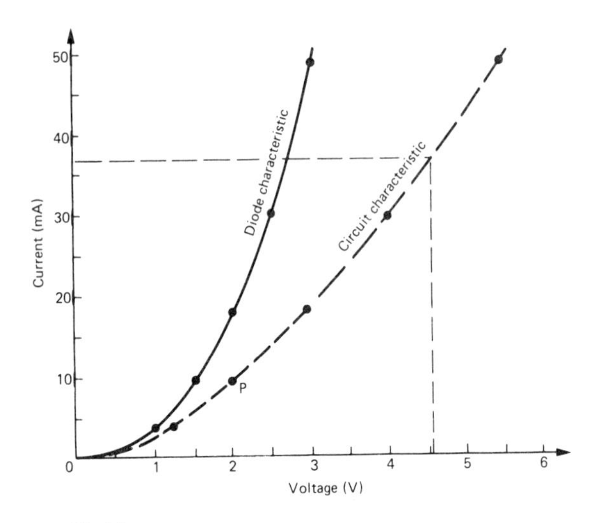

Fig 13

To draw the characteristic of the complete circuit requires us to find the value of the *applied* voltage which, with the 50 Ω resistor connected in series with the diode, gives the stated diode voltage at the particular value of diode (or circuit) current.

We take, as an example, the circuit condition when the diode voltage is 1.5 V and the current through it is, from the table, 9.8 mA; (see *Fig 14*). We require the voltage V_R across the resistor.

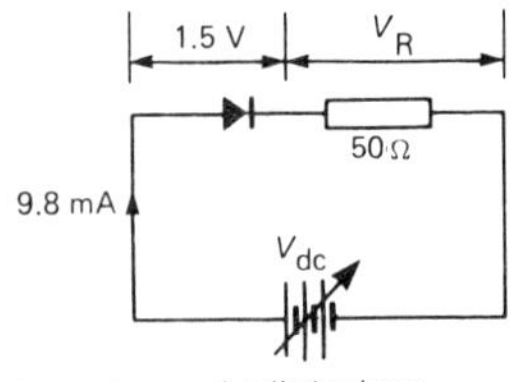

Fig 14

This is

$$V_R = I.R = 9.8 \times 10^{-3} \times 50$$
$$= 0.49 \text{ V}$$

Hence the applied voltage is

$$V_{dc} = 0.49 + 1.5 = 1.99 \text{ V}$$

This gives us one point on the circuit characteristic, this point is plotted at P on the diagram.

In an exactly similar way, the other points can be calculated and for the current range considered; they are

Current (mA)	0	0.9	4.0	9.8	18.2	30.0	48.0
Applied voltage (V_{dc})	0	0.55	1.2	1.99	2.91	4.0	5.4

The complete circuit characteristic is shown in dotted line. Reading from this, when the applied voltage is 4.5 V, the current is about 37 mA.

C FURTHER PROBLEMS ON THE *p-n* JUNCTION DIODE

(a) SHORT ANSWER PROBLEMS (answers on page 132)

(answers on page 132)

1 Explain the meaning of the following terms:
(a) depletion layer;
(b) barrier potential;
(c) reverse saturation current;
(d) diffusion;
(e) hole-electron pairs.

2 Complete the following statements:
(a) Semiconductor material is normally electrically . . . .
(b) Diffusion current is due to the movement of . . . . carriers.
(c) The *p*-region of a *p-n* diode corresponds to the . . . .
(d) In *n*-type material there are a large number of . . . . donated by the . . . . atoms plus a number of thermally generated . . . .
(e) When a diode is forward biased, the leakage current flows in the . . . . direction to/as the main current.
(f) The rate of increase of leakage current with temperature rise is greater in . . . . than in . . . .
(g) An ideal diode would have . . . . forward resistance and . . . . reverse resistance.
(h) The power dissipated in an ideal diode would be . . . .

3 Say whether the following statements are true or false:
(a) A semiconductor diode has two junctions.
(b) Diffusion causes the *p*-side of a junction to become negative with respect to the *n*-side.
(c) Leakage current is the result of intrinsic action only.
(d) The potential barrier at a *p-n* junction behaves as if it were in series with an external battery.
(e) Diffusion current changes with barrier potential.
(f) The current flowing in circuit wires external to a *p-n* junction consists always of electrons.
(g) Diffusion always involves charged particles.

4 The leakage current of a certain germanium diode is 5 μA at 25°C. What will be the leakage approximately at 55°C?

5 A silicon diode has a leakage current of 0.01 μA at 20°C. Find its approximate value at 100°C.

(b) MULTI–CHOICE PROBLEMS (answers on page 132)

1 In forward bias, the *p*-region of a semiconductor diode is
(a) positive with respect to the *n*-region;
(b) negative with respect to the *n*-region;
(c) at the same potential as the *n*-region.

2 The voltage drop across a silicon *p-n* junction when it is conducting is
(a) about 200 mV; (b) about 600 mV; (c) zero; (d) indeterminate.

3 The flow of minority carriers across the depletion layer:
(a) strengthens the field across the junction;
(b) weakens the field across the junction;
(c) has no effect on the field;
(d) eliminates the field completely.

4 A piece of *p*-type semiconductor material is
(a) negatively charged; (b) positively charged; (c) neutral.

5 The current flow through a piece of pure semiconductor is carried by
(a) free electrons; (b) free holes; (c) equal numbers of free electrons and holes.

6 The reverse current in a silicon diode at a given temperature is
(a) much greater than in a germanium diode;
(b) much less than in a germanium diode;
(c) the same as in a germanium diode;
(d) dependent upon the impurity concentration.

(c) CONVENTIONAL PROBLEMS

1 By reference to the formation of a potential barrier and to a current-voltage characteristic, explain the rectifying action of a *p-n* junction diode.

2 The static resistance of a diode is the ratio V/I at a particular point. The dynamic resistance is the *slope* of the characteristic at a particular point. From the characteristic of *Fig 15* estimate the static and dynamic resistance of the diode at
(a) 0.4 V forward biasing; (b) 1.0 V forward biasing.

[(a) 70 Ω; (b) 25 Ω]

3 Name two semiconductor materials and compare their properties in relation to
(a) a good conductor such as copper; (b) a good insulator such as rubber.

4 Draw a *p-n* junction and show the polarity of the potential barrier set up.

5 Draw a *p-n* junction and show the polarity of the applied voltage for
(a) forward bias; (b) reverse bias.

6 Sketch a diagram showing how you would use:
(a) a voltmeter; (b) a milliammeter; (c) a d.c. supply; (d) a potentiometer in a circuit for the tracing of a static characteristic of a *p-n* junction diode.

7 The two diodes shown in *Fig 16* can be assumed to have zero forward resistance and infinite reverse resistance. Calculate the currents flowing in each branch of the circuit (a) when the battery is connected as shown; (b) when the battery is reversed.

[(a) 2 A; $3\frac{1}{3}$ A, O; (b) 2 A, O, $2\frac{1}{2}$ A]

8 A waveform which switches periodically above and below earth potential is shown in *Fig 17*. If this waveform is applied to the input terminals of the circuit shown in the figure, sketch the output waveform you would expect to appear across the resistor R, indicating the voltage levels reached.

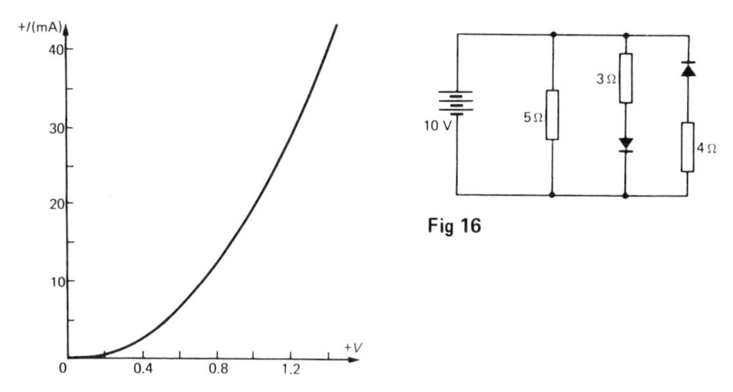

Fig 15

Fig 16

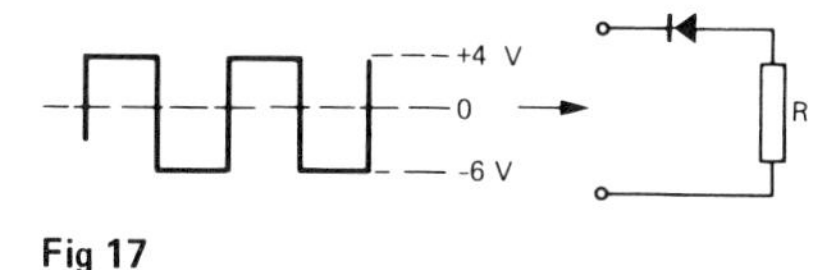

Fig 17

9 *Fig 18* shows two simple diode circuits.
Calculate (i) the current I flowing in circuit (a); (ii) the voltage across the resistor in circuit (b).

[(i) 10 mA; (ii) OV]

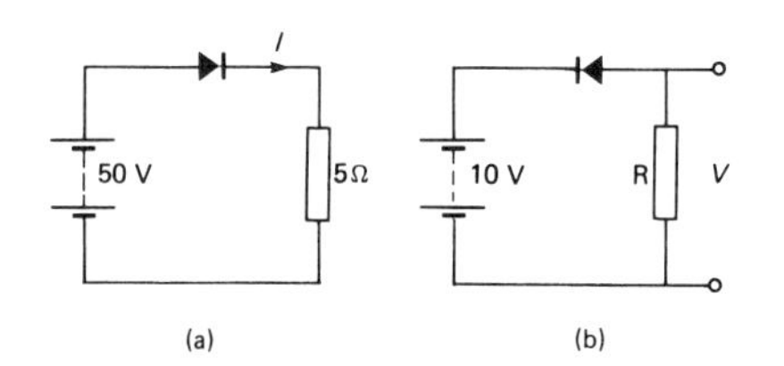

Fig 18

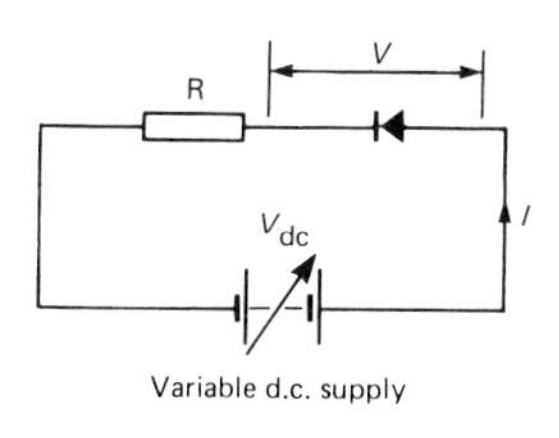

Fig 19

10 The circuit of *Fig 19* was used to measure the forward-bias characteristic of a silicon. The following table of values was recorded in the experiment:

V_{dc}	0	0.76	1.00	1.24	1.49	1.72	1.96	2.20
I (mA)	0	2.00	4.00	6.00	8.00	10.0	12.0	14.0
V	0	0.60	0.68	0.76	0.85	0.93	1.00	1.07

Plot the diode characteristic. If $V_{dc} = V + IR$, obtain a value for the resistor R used in this circuit.

[$R = 80\ \Omega$]

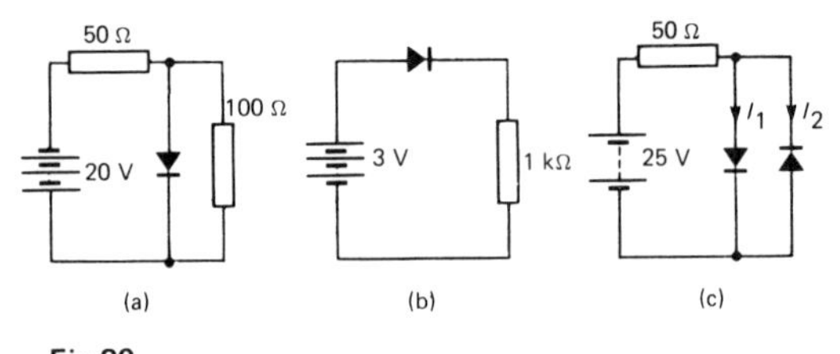

Fig 20

11 The diodes shown in *Fig 20* are silicon. Calculate:
(i) the current flowing in the 100 Ω resistor of diagram (a);
(ii) the voltage across the 1 kΩ resistor of diagram (b);
(iii) the currents I_1 and I_2 of diagram (c).
[(i) 133 mA; (ii) 2.4 V; (iii) 0.488 A, O]

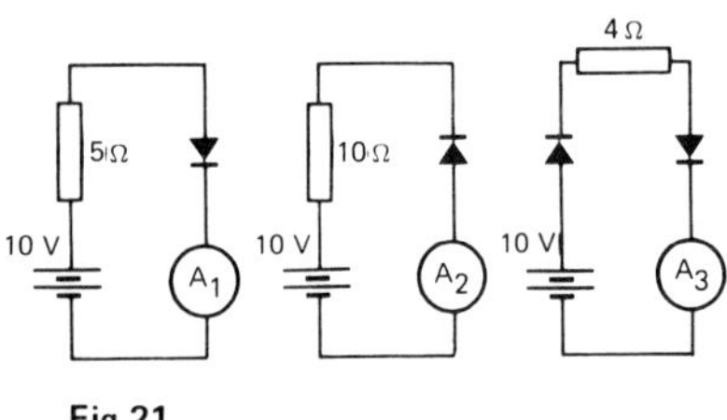

Fig 21

12 In *Fig 21* the diodes are considered ideal. What will the ammeters A_1, A_2 and A_3 read?
[A_1 = 2A; A_2 = 0; A_3 = 2.5 A]

3 Diode applications

A. MAIN POINTS CONCERNED WITH BASIC DIODE APPLICATIONS

1 (i) Almost all electronic equipment operates from steady d.c. supplies. In cases where the power requirements are small, such supplies are obtained from cells or batteries. Where power requirements are large, however, the mains electricity supply is used and this necessitates the conversion of the alternating current (or voltage) of this supply into the direct current (or voltage) required by the apparatus. Such conversion is known as **rectification** and when a suitable circuit element is used for this purpose, it is known as a **rectifier**.

(ii) An alternating current is one which flows first in one direction along a conductor and then, after a given time, reverses its direction and flows for a further period of time in the opposite direction. The most familiar example of alternating current is shown in *Fig 1(a)* where the sinusoidal wave is displayed. Such a complete

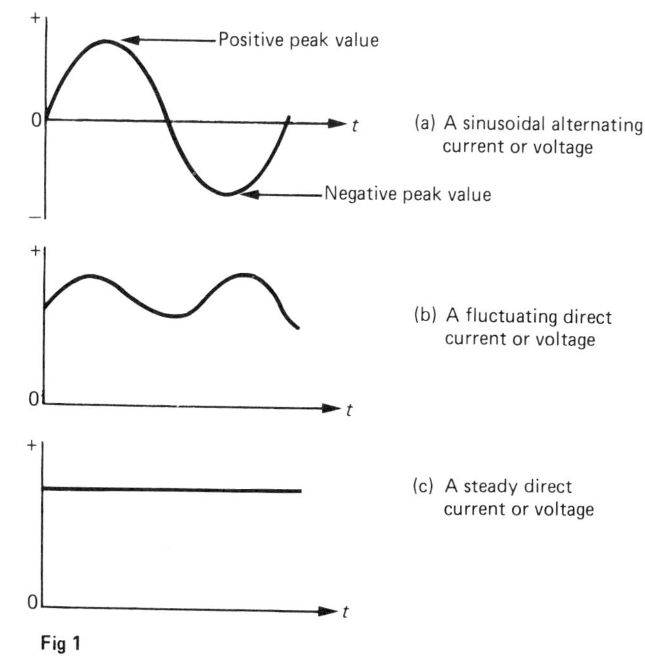

Fig 1

backwards and forwards movement of the charge carriers (electrons in this case) represents one cycle of the alternating quantity.

In relation to such an alternating current, a direct current flows always in one direction, though it is not necessarily a steady current. *Fig 1(b)* shows a fluctuating direct current. This might be confused with the alternating current at (a), but the direct current never crosses the horizontal axis.

A steady direct current is shown in *Fig 1(c)*. This is the kind of output we want after the alternating quantity shown at (a) has been rectified. To convert the alternating wave into a one-way or **unidirectional** variation it is necessary to eliminate one half of either of the alternations. The resulting curve must therefore lie wholly above the horizontal or zero axis or wholly below it, but it must not cross it. *Fig 2* shows what we expect the rectifier system to do: not only

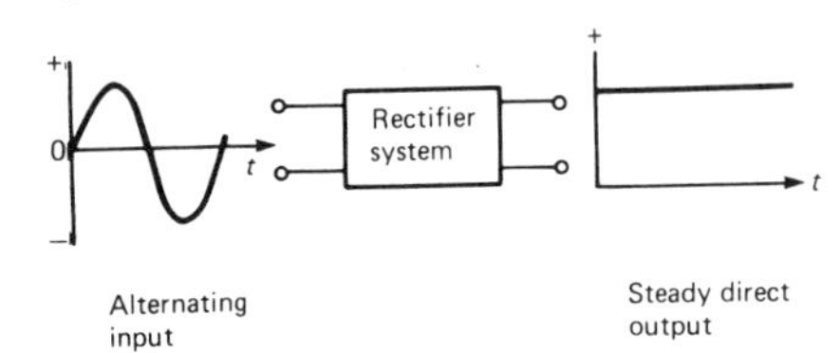

Fig 2

must one half of the alternations be removed but the output must be smoothed to a steady level.

(iii) The simplest type of rectifier is a circuit element which performs the function of an automatic swtich. A perfect rectifier would have zero resistance in one direction and infinite resistance in the other. Clearly, the one-way *p-n* junction diode will provide a very good approximation to these requirements.

2 In the majority of power supplies, a transformer is used between the mains terminals and the actual rectifier circuit. This performs two functions: it isolates the equipment being supplied from direct connection to the mains supply, and it enables the mains voltage to be either stepped up or stepped down to the level suited to the apparatus for which the rectified supply will be finally needed.

3 (i) A simple **half-wave rectifier** circuit is shown in *Fig 3*. The diode allows current to flow through the load resistor R_L only when terminal A of the transformer secon-

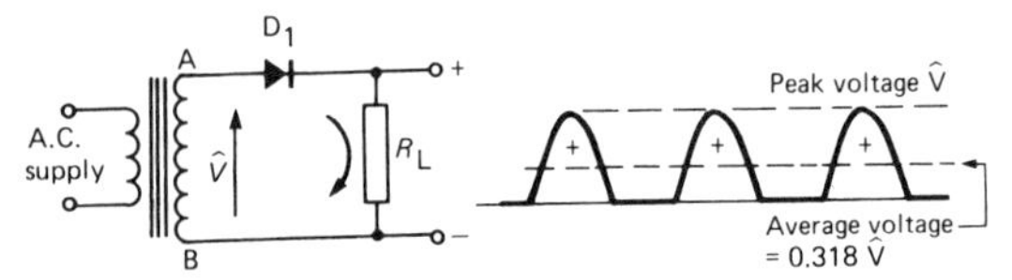

Fig 3

dary winding is positive with respect to B, cutting off when A is negative with respect to B. The current flow in R_L is therefore always in one direction, so the waveform of the voltage developed across R_L will be that shown in the diagram. Notice that the peak value of the output wave is equal to the peak value of the alternating input voltage from the transformer, V. The average value of the output is then 0.318 V.

(ii) The half-wave rectifier has the disadvantage that there is no output at all for half of the available input. *Fig 4* shows an improved rectifier circuit which makes use of the whole of the a.c. waveform. This is known as a **full-wave rectifier**. Two diodes are used and the transformer has a secondary winding of double the normal voltage but with a centre tap C. We can treat this centre tap as being a

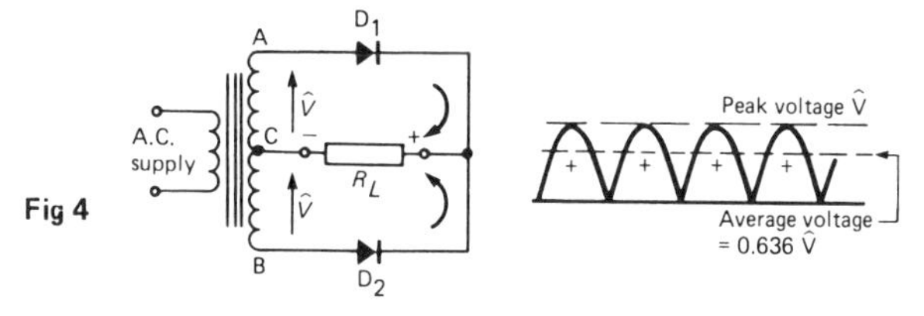

Fig 4

neutral point. As a result the instantaneous voltages at the outer ends of the winding are always 180° out of phase. Each diode therefore conducts in turn when its particular anode happens to be positive with respect to the centre point C.

On the first half cycle A is positive relative to C. D_1 conducts to the right hand side of the load resistor R_L. On the following half cycle A is negative and B is positive to C. Hence D_2 conducts also to the right hand side of the load. What we really have is two half-wave rectifier circuits connected to a single load resistor, the spaces between the half-sine waves developed by either diode now being filled in by the other diode. As before, the peak value of the putput wave is equal to the peak value of the alternating input voltage from each half of the secondary winding, but the average output voltage has now doubled to 0.636 V. It is clear from the diagram that the full-wave d.c. waveform is of a more continuous nature than was that of the half-wave example.

4 *Fig 5* shows a different form of full-wave rectifier. This circuit uses four diodes but does not require a centre-tapped transformer winding. Because it is reminiscent of the shape of a Wheatstone bridge network, this particular circuit is indeed known as a **bridge rectifier**. Nowadays, it is used instead of the previously described circuit because diodes are available very cheaply and the cost and bulk of an additional transformer winding is avoided. In many cases, bridge rectifiers are sold as a complete block of four diodes suitably encapsulated.

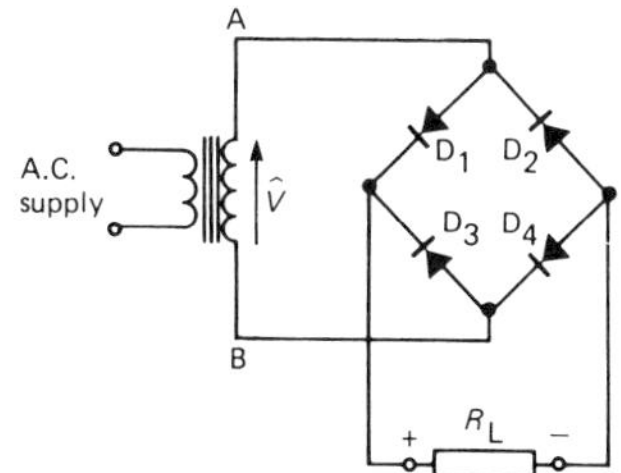

Fig 5

In the bridge circuit the diodes conduct in series-pairs. When the secondary terminal A is positive with respect to B, diodes D_1 and D_3 conduct in series but diodes D_2 and D_4 are cut off. When the input polarity reverses, D_2 and D_4 switch on in series but D_1 and D_3 switch off. Following the flow of current through the circuit in each case shows that the flow through the load resistor is always in the direction indicated. Once again a unidirectional current is obtained and so the voltage developed across the load exhibits a definite polarity.

5 (i) Although the fundamental action of any diode is its ability to permit current to pass through it in only one direction, diodes are manufactured in a very wide range of voltage and current ratings. These ratings must be taken into account when diodes are being chosen for use in particular rectifier configurations.

(ii) A diode has a small forward resistance when it is conducting and a very high but not infinite reverse resistance when it is cut off. When current passes through the diode, either as a relatively large forward current or as a small reverse current, power is dissipated in the resistance concerned.

This dissipation will appear as heat, exactly as it would in an ordinary resistor, so there will be an increase in the junction temperature. This local heating must not be allowed to become appreciable because leakage current increases with temperature rise and an excessive leakage current can lead to a destructive breakdown of the junction. For this reason, diodes intended for use in circuits where the current may exceed a few amperes, are made either with wire ends of relatively heavy gauge wire to conduct away the heat or are assembled in metal cases provided with a means of bolting them down to large area metal plates which can act as **heat radiators** or heat **sinks.** *Fig 6* shows a typical high power rectifier diode.

(iii) There is also the factor of the reverse breakdown voltage of the rectifier to be considered. The peak inverse voltage (p.i.v. or V_{RRM}) is the maximum reverse bias voltage to which a diode should be subjected in a particular circuit application. The manufacturer quotes a maximum value of the p.i.v. to which a particular diode is designed. A rectifier diode must never be used in a circuit where the applied reverse voltage can exceed the figure stated by the manufacturer.

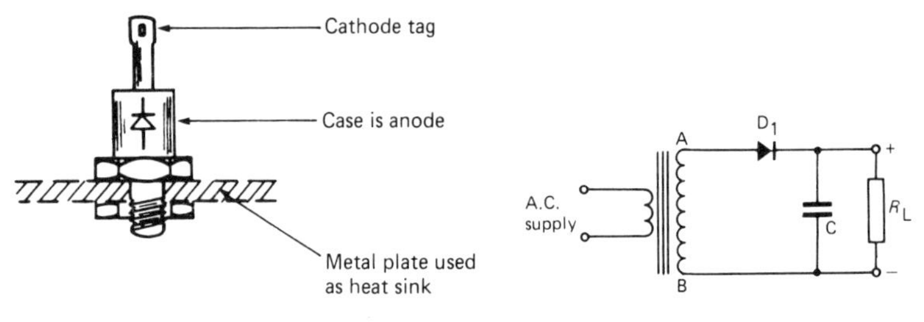

Fig 6 **Fig 7**

6 (i) The output waveforms obtained from the half- and full-wave rectifiers, though unidirectional, are still far from being the steady voltages we would obtain from batteries. Car batteries and the like can be directly charged from such fluctuating waveforms, but the large alternating component prevent them being used directly to supply electronic equipment such as amplifiers.

To iron out all the variations and smooth the waveform, a reservoir capacitor, C, is connected across the rectifier output, as shown in *Fig 7*. The value of C for use with a 50 Hz mains supply may range from 100 μF to 500 μF or more, depending upon the load current required and the degree of smoothing acceptable.

(ii) Consider what happens during the first positive half-cycle of output after switching on. The capacitor will charge up to the peak value of the rectifier output voltage, that is, to $\hat{V}$. During the interval represented by the missing negative half-cycle, no further charge is added to C and it partially discharges through the load resistor R_L. However, if R_L is of large value, the fall in voltage across C before the arrival of the next positive half cycle will be small. The capacitor will then be 'topped-up' by the tip of this half-cycle and the voltage restored.

This continual replenishment of the charge on C will maintain the voltage across its terminals at a value very close to the peak value of the output waveform. The output waveform now is as shown in *Fig 8* in solid line, with the mean d.c. value as a dotted line. The corresponding half cycles of the original unsmoothed waveform are drawn in broken line.

You will notice two important points: (a) the waveform shown in solid line is very much smoother than it was before the capacitor was added; (b) the average voltage across the load resistor is much greater. The best smoothing

Fig 8

effect is obtained when the value of R_L (which represents the apparatus being supplied) is extremely large for then there is negligible discharge between the output half cycles and the almost steady d.c. output approximates very closely to $\hat{V}$ in amplitude. When R_L is small, the discharge becomes large and the output voltage is rippled. Notice from *Fig 3* diagram the meaning of **ripple voltage**. The greater the capacity of C for a given value of R_L, the more effective the smoothing effect, and the smaller the ripple voltage.

By the use of a full-wave rectifier circuit, the smoothing effect is improved considerably, for the time over which the capacitor can discharge between the half cycles is halved, and so, for given component values, the ripple voltage is halved also.

(iii) When a smoothing capacitor is added to a rectifier output, the p.i.v. conditions need to be reviewed. A further look at the half-wave rectifier of *Fig 3* will illustrate this. When the diode is reverse biased, no current flows in R_L, hence the applied voltage appears solely across the diode. The p.i.v. is therefore equal to V. This means that the diode breakdown voltage must be greater than V, i.e. *not* the r.m.s. value of voltage in which the transformer output will be normally stated.

Now consider the case of the same circuit with the capacitor added (*Fig 7*). When end A of the transformer secondary is negative, the diode will be switched off but the capacitor at the diode cathode is charged up very nearly to the positive peak value of the alternating voltage, $\hat{V}$. Since the diode anode is then subjected to a negative value of $\hat{V}$ from the transformer, the total voltage acting across the diode is 2 V. This means that the diode breakdown rating must now be greater than 2 $\hat{V}$ for the circuit to work without damage. The same argument clearly applies to the full-wave rectifier illustrated in *Fig 4*.

7 (i) Even when the output is adequately smoothed, the above mentioned rectifier circuits are not always suitable for supplying direct current to a load. The main reasons for this are:

(a) The output voltage changes if the mains input voltage varies;

(b) The output voltage changes if the load conditions vary.

(c) The ripple voltage in the output increases as the current demand of the load increases.

Such supplies are said to be **unstabilized** against these variations. A **stabilized** supply, on the other hand, is designed to reduce ripple to a minimum and to provide an output voltage that is constant regardless of mains voltage or load current variations.

(ii) The basic voltage regulator circuit exploits the reverse breakdown properties of the *p-n* junction as discussed in chapter 1, where the **zener diode** was mentioned. In this diode, high doping levels lead to artificially low reverse breakdown voltages,

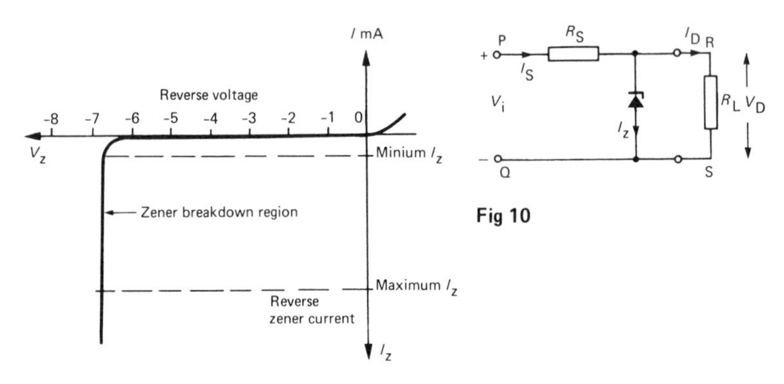

Fig 10

Fig 9

so that a typical characteristic would be as shown in *Fig 9* where breakdown occurs at 6.8 V. Such an element can be used as a voltage regulator if it is connected to the rectifier output terminals as illustrated in *Fig 10*.

We notice that the diode is connected into the circuit so that it is reverse biased. At this particular voltage for which it has been designed, the diode will break down and thereafter, as the characteristic shows, the voltage across the junction remains substantially constant, irrespective of the current flowing throught the junction. This reverse flow would be destructive in an unprotected diode but here it is limited to a safe value by the series resistor R_s. Provided that the voltage across the zener does not fall below the breakdown value, the diode behaves as a current reservoir. Referring to *Fig 10*, it is not difficult to understand how the diode provides a constant output voltage V_o at terminals R and S in spite of any variations in either the supply voltage V_i at terminals P and Q or in the load current I_o flowing through R_L. Suppose the d.c. input voltage at P–Q increases for some reason, then the current through the zener increases but as the voltage across it remains constant, the increase in voltage appears across R_s. Conversely, if the d.c. input voltage decreases, the Zener surrenders the extra current and the voltage across R_s falls. In, either case the input variation is absorbed by resistor R_s and the desired voltage at R–S remains constant.

Suppose now the load current I_o increases for some reason. The Zener current will decrease by the same amount. Similarly, if the load current decreases, the Zener current will increase by the same amount. This time the Zener takes up the excess current and sheds the current difference demanded by the load, so acting as a current reservoir while maintaining a constant voltage at the output terminals.

We notice from the characteristic of *Fig 9* that there is a minimum value of zener current I_Z for which the diode will operate effectively as a stabilizer. The zener current must not be allowed to fall below this. Similarly, there is a maximum value of current which is determined by the power rating of the zener, such that

$$V_Z \cdot I_{Z(max)} = P_{(max)} \text{ i.e. } I_{Z(max)} = \frac{P_{max}}{V_Z}$$

The rectified output supplies both the load current I_o and I_Z. Hence

Supply current $I_s = I_Z + I_o$

When the load current is low the zener draws more current but this must never exceed $I_{Z(max)}$. The corresponding minimum value of I_o is then

$$I_{o(min)} = I_s - I_{Z(max)}$$

When the load current is high the zener draws less current but this must never fall below $I_{Z(min)}$. The maximum value of I_o is then

$$I_{o(max)} = I_s - I_{Z(min)}$$

General purpose diodes are readily available in a range of breakdown voltages running from about 2.5 V up to some 200 V, with power ratings ranging from 400 mW up to 20 W and more

B. WORKED PROBLEMS ON BASIC DIODE APPLICATIONS

Problem 1. Explain why an ideal diode would be loss free. How does a real diode differ from such an ideal diode?

An ideal diode would have zero resistance in the forward direction and infinite resistance in the reverse direction. Hence, under conditions of forward bias, the voltage developed across it would be zero irrespective of the current flowing. In the reverse direction the current flowing through it would be zero irrespective of the magnitude of the impressed voltage. In both cases, since power is represented by the product VI, the power dissipated would be zero. So the ideal diode would be loss free.

A real diode has a small but finite forward resistance and a large but finite reverse resistance, so power must be dissipated within the element. Such a diode can be represented as an ideal diode having a small value resistor R_f connected in series with it to represent the actual forward resistance, and with a large value resistor R_r connected in parallel to represent the actual reverse resistance, see *Fig 11*.

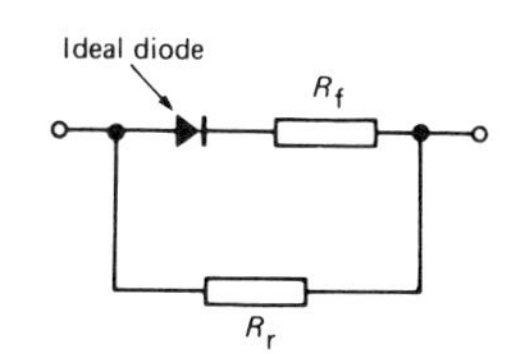

Fig 11

> *Problem 2.* In the bridge rectifier circuit of *Fig 12* what is the greatest reverse voltage applied to any of the diodes?

Consider the instant when the applied voltage is at its peak value $\hat{V}$ and terminal A is positive. The voltage across the load resistor will be $\hat{V}$ with the polarity shown, diodes D_1 and D_3 now conducting. If we follow around the circuit points AEDFCB through series diodes D_2 and D_4 which are now reverse biased and switched off, we see that the load voltage adds to the transformer voltage at this instant to give a total of 2 $\hat{V}$ across these diodes. But since this voltage is shared between D_2 and D_4 in series, the p.i.v. per diode is simply $\hat{V}$.

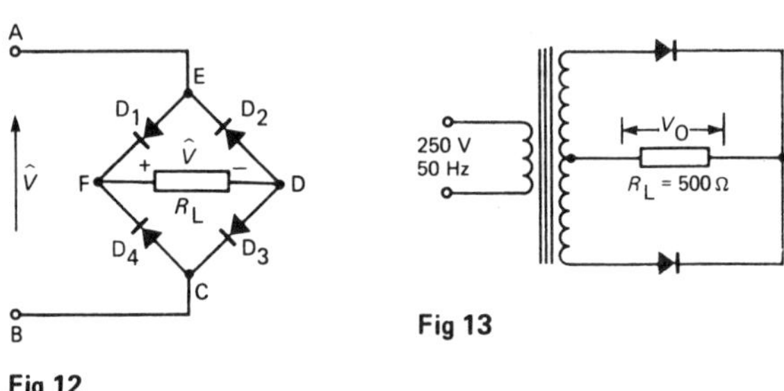

Fig 12

Fig 13

> *Problem 3.* The full-wave rectifier shown in *Fig 13* is supplied from a 250 V, 50 Hz point by way of a step-down transformer of overall turns ratio 5:1. Calculate (a) the peak voltage across either half of the secondary winding; (b) the peak and average values of the current flowing through the resistor; (c) the peak and average values of the output voltage V_o. Assume ideal diodes and transformer.

First of all, since the transformer steps down the primary voltage in the ratio 5:1, the overall secondary voltage will be 250/5 = 50 V r.m.s. So each half of the winding will generate 25 V r.m.s.

(a) Since peak voltage = r.m.s. voltage $\times \sqrt{2}$, the peak secondary voltage will be $25 \times \sqrt{2} = 35.36$ V for each half winding.

(b) The load resistor $R_L = 500\ \Omega$. Peak current through this load will coincide with peak voltage across it, hence

$$I_{dc} = 35.36/500 = 0.071\ \text{A} = 71\ \text{mA}$$

The average current will then be $0.636\ I_{dc}$

$= 0.636 \times 71 =$ **45.15 mA**

(c) The peak output voltage will be the same as the peak input since the diodes are assumed ideal. Hence

$$V_o = 35.36\ \text{V}$$

Hence the average output voltage = $0.636 \times 35.36 =$ **22.5 V**

Problem 4. Explain what is meant by the slope resistance of a zener diode. What would be the slope resistance of a zener if (a) the linear resistance region was precisely vertical; (b) a change of 30 mV resulted when the current changed from 3 mA to 5 mA?

The simple shunt Zener stabilizer circuit of *Fig 10* can never stabilize the output voltage exactly. The effectiveness of the circuit depends upon the steepness of the characteristic beyond the breakdown point; this can be expressed as a slope resistance, for referring to *Fig 14*

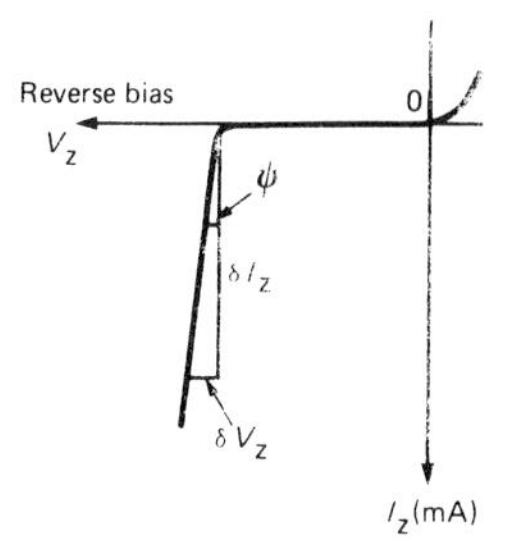

Fig 14

$$\text{Slope resistance } R_Z = \frac{\delta V_Z}{\delta I_Z} = \tan \psi \text{ ohms}$$

Since ψ is clearly a small angle, the slope resistance will be small. So the diode behaves after breakdown as a linear resistance and this part of its characteristic is known as the **linear resistance** region.

(a) If the characteristic was perfectly vertical, ψ would be zero, hence the slope resistance would be zero. In the case, the stabilization would be perfect.

(b) Here the change in $V_Z = \delta V_Z = 30$ mV and the change in $I_Z = \delta I_Z = (5 - 3)$mA $= 2$ mA. Hence

$$\text{Slope resistance } R_Z = \frac{30 \times 10^{-3}}{2 \times 10^{-3}} = \mathbf{15\Omega}$$

Problem 5. A 20 V stabilized supply is required from a 40 V d.c. unstabilized source. A 20 V zener diode is available having a power rating of 1.5 W. Find the required value of series resistor R_s in the circuit of *Fig 15*.

The Zener must be protected by R_s so that the greatest current that can flow through it at its rated breakdown voltage of 20 V will not cause the power dissipation to exceed 1.5 W. Clearly, the zener current will be greatest when the load current is zero. So

$$\text{Maximum current} = \frac{P}{V_Z} = \frac{1.5}{20} = 0.075 \text{ A}$$

To stabilize at 20 V from a 40 V input, the voltage drop across R_s must be (40–20), i.e. 20 V. Hence

$$R_s = \frac{20}{0.075} = \mathbf{267\ \Omega}$$

C. FURTHER PROBLEMS ON BASIC DIODE APPLICATIONS

(a) SHORT ANSWER PROBLEMS (answers on page 132)

1 Explain the meaning of the following terms: (a) peak inverse voltage; (b) half-wave rectifier; (c) bridge rectifier; (d) heat sink; (e) reservoir capacitor; (f) stabilized output; (g) ripple voltage.

2 Complete the following:
(a) An ideal diode has .... forward resistance and .... reverse resistance.
(b) The power dissipated in ideal diode is ....
(c) A bridge rectifier uses .... diodes.
(d) The average output voltage from an unsmoothed half-wave rectifier is about .... of the peak voltage.
(e) The addition of a smoothing capacitor to the output of a two element full-wave rectifier .... the p.i.v. across the diodes.

3 Differentiate between (a) the p.i.v. of a diode in a given circuit; (b) the p.i.v. rating of a diode.

4 A diode has a peak inverse voltage rating of 300 V. Could this diode be used as a half-wave rectifier with a transformer whose stated secondary voltage is 240 V r.m.s.?

5 A diode has a reverse breakdown voltage of 50 V. It is used in (a) a half-wave rectifier circuit; (b) a two element full-wave rectifier circuit. For an unsmoothed output, what is the maximum permissible value of V in each case?

6 Assuming an otherwise ideal diode, what would be the effect on the current flowing in the load of a resistance placed (a) in series with the diode; (b) in parallel with the diode?

7 Say whether the following statements are false or true:
(a) In a stabilizing circuit, the anode of a zener diode is connected to the positive terminal.
(b) When a diode is used as a rectifier, its cathode terminal provides the positive pole of the d.c. output.
(c) A zener diode will stabilize even when the current through it falls to zero.
(d) The breakdown voltage of a zener diode depends upon the doping level.
(e) If a leakage current flowed in the reverse direction through a rectifier in a half-wave circuit, the p.i.v. would be reduced by the magnitude of the voltage drop in the resistance.
(f) For a given load current and smoothing capacitor, the ripple voltage of a full-wave circuit is about half that obtained in a half-wave circuit.

(b) MULTI-CHOICE PROBLEMS (answers on page 132)

1 A reservoir capacitor should have a voltage rating not less than
(a) $\hat{V}$; (b) $2\hat{V}$; (c) $\sqrt{2}\hat{V}$.

2 A full-wave rectifier circuit having a 50 Hz a.c. input will have a ripple voltage of frequency
(a) 25 Hz; (b) 50 Hz; (c) 100 Hz; (d) 200 Hz.

3 In a Zener stabilizing circuit, the power dissipated in the diode is greatest when the load current is
(a) greatest; (b) small but not zero; (c) zero.

4 The d.c. output polarity from a half-wave rectifier will be reversed if
(a) the diode is reversed;
(b) the transformer primary winding is reversed;
(c) the transformer secondary winding is reversed;
(d) both windings are reversed.

5 If a resistance equal in value to the load resistance is connected in parallel with the diode in a half-wave rectifier circuit,
(a) the output voltage will be doubled;
(b) the output voltage will be halved;
(c) the circuit will stop rectifying.

6 If a resistance equal in value to the load resistance is connected in series with the diode in a half-wave rectifier circuit.
(a) the output voltage will be doubled; (b) the output voltage will be halved;
(c) the circuit will stop rectifying.

7 In a two-diode full-wave rectifier the p.i.v. across either of the diodes is
(a) equal to the peak supply voltage; (b) equal to twice the peak supply voltage;
(c) equal to the output voltage; (d) equal to twice the output voltage.

8 In any rectifier circuit the forward resistance of the diodes will
(a) decrease the output voltage slightly; (b) increase the output voltage slightly;
(c) have no effect on the output voltage.

(c) CONVENTIONAL PROBLEMS

1 A rectifier diode has a constant forward resistance of 5 Ω and a reverse resistance which may be considered infinite. For a 50 V peak a.c. input and a 100 Ω load resistor, calculate for a half-wave rectifier (a) the average current flowing in the load; (b) the average load voltage; (c) the average voltage across the diode.
[(a) 0.176 A; (b) 17.6 V; (c) 0.9 V]

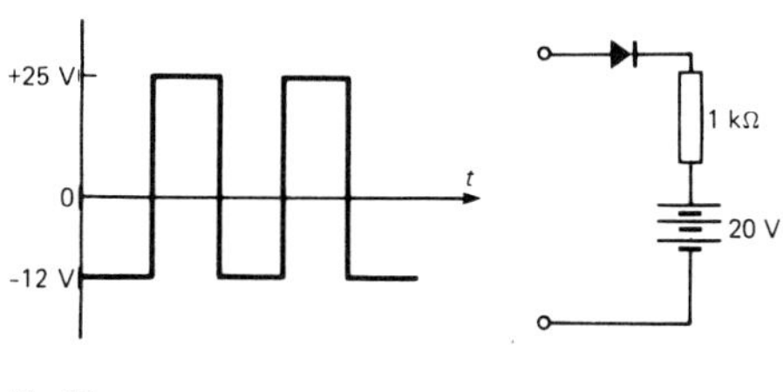

Fig 16

2 The square wave shown in *Fig 16* is applied to the rectifier system shown. Find (a) the p.i.v. applied to the diode; (b) the current flowing in the 1 kΩ load resistor.
[(a) 32 V; (b) 5 mA]

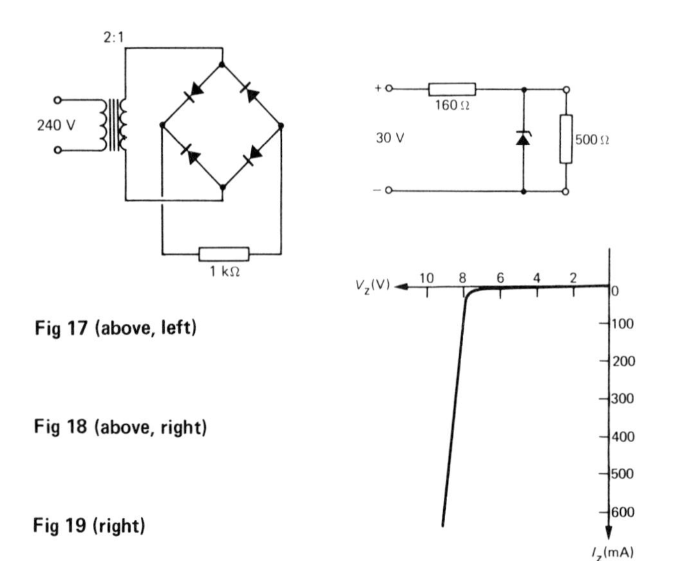

Fig 17 (above, left)

Fig 18 (above, right)

Fig 19 (right)

3 A sinusoidal voltage represented by $v = 100 \sin 200\,\pi t$ volts is applied to a circuit made up of an ideal diode in series with a 50 Ω resistor. What is (a) the r.m.s. value of the supply voltage; (b) the average value of the rectified voltage; (c) the ripple frequency?

[(a) 70.7 V; (b) 31.8 V; (c) 50 Hz

4 Calculate the peak and average values of load current in the bridge rectifier of *Fig 17* assuming ideal diodes. If a capacitor of large value is connected across the load resistor, what will be the new value of load current, approximately?

[0.17 A; 0.107 A; 0.17 A]

5 Draw a circuit diagram of a simple zener diode stabilising circuit and explain how it operates to maintain a constant voltage output across a load resistor.

6 In the circuit of *Fig 18* the zener breakdown voltage is 20 V. Assuming that breakdown has occurred, what will be the current in the 500 Ω load resistor and in the zener?

[40 mA; 22.5 mA]

7 Using the zener characteristic of *Fig 19* determine as accurately as possible (a) the zener breakdown voltage; (b) the slope resistance; (c) the change in output voltage when the zener current changes from 100 mA to 500 mA; (d) the minimum zener current.

[(a) 7.5 V; (b) 2.5 Ω; (c) 1 V; (d) 50 m

8 The zener diode of the previous problem is used as a stabiliser to supply a load whose current varies between 150 mA and 350 mA. If the supply voltage is fixed at 15 V and the zener is not to fall below its minimum current figure, what least values of series resistor will be required?

[17.5 Ω]

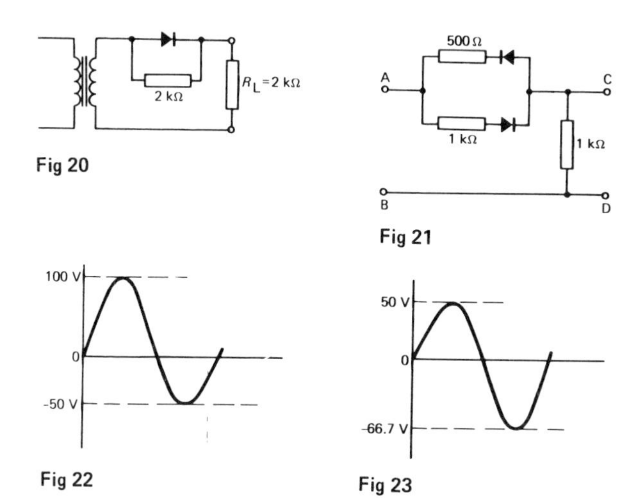

Fig 20

Fig 21

Fig 22

Fig 23

9 A 20 V stabilised supply is required from a 50 V d.c. input. A 20 V zener is used having a power rating of 2 W. Find the required value of series resistor.

[300 Ω]

If the zener stabilizes down to a current of 5 mA, calculate the greatest and least supply voltage between which stabilization will be achieved, for a load resistor of 1 kΩ.

[56 V; 27.5 V]

10 In the circuit of *Fig 20* the transformer secondary produces a 100 V peak sine wave. Sketch the waveform appearing across the load resistor R_L.

[see *Fig 22*]

11 A 100 V peak sinusoidal voltage is applied to terminals A–B in *Fig 21*. What will be the waveform across terminals C–D?

[see *Fig 23*]

4 Bipolar transistors and their characteristics

A. MAIN POINTS CONCERNED WITH BIPOLAR TRANSISTORS AND THEIR CHARACTERISTICS

1 The **bipolar transistor** is a semiconductor device which can act as an amplifier as well as a switch which is the basic property of a diode. The name, 'transistor' is a combination of the two words 'transfer' and 'resistor'. This is because transistor operation depends upon the fact that a current generated in a circuit of low resistance can be transferred to a circuit of high resistance and hence a power gain can be obtained.

In comparison with the thermionic valve which has been replaced by the transistor in all but high power and microwave applications, the transistor has the advantages of low operating voltages and small physical size. The discrete transistor is itself many times smaller than even the most miniature of valves, and in the form of the **packaged integrated microcircuit** many hundreds of transistors are accommodated on a chip of silicon material measuring only a few square millimetres in area.

2 Although it involves an older method of fabrication, the bipolar transistor made by what was known as the diffused alloy junction process, illustrates both the basic form that a transistor takes and its operation. This is shown in *Fig 1*.

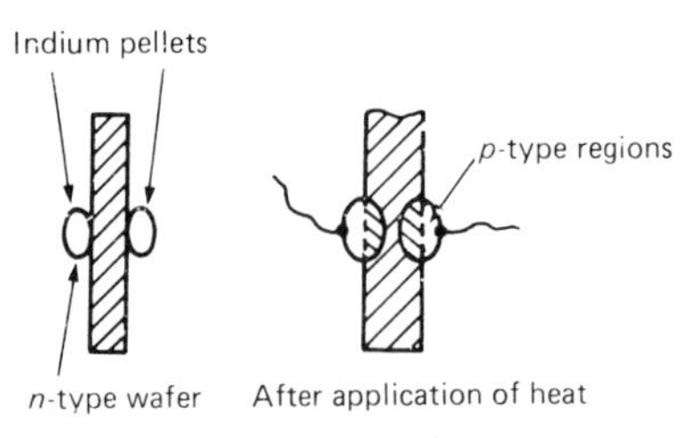

Fig 1

A thin slice of germanium of high purity and in single crystal form was lightly doped with a pentavalent impurity, turning it into *n*-type material. Both surfaces of the wafer were then converted to a carefully controlled depth, to *p*-type material. This was accomplished by placing a small pellet of the trivalent metal indium on each surface of the wafer and applying heat so that the two pellets alloyed with the germanium.

On cooling, the alloy re-crystalised, leaving a small but sufficient amount of *p*-type impurity in the wafer material by the process of overdoping. Conducting wires of a material which did not produce either *p*- or *n*-type material were then attracted to the two indium pellets and to the wafer between them. After suitable cleaning, the assembly was placed in a small hermetically sealed glass case which was blackened to exclude incident light (which would affect the transistor operation). The three connecting leads were taken out through the base of the case. Such a transistor is a *p-n-p* transistor since it is formed of a sandwich in that order.

Modern transistors are made by an improved technique which enables a very large quantity to be turned out at one time and *n-p-n* sandwiches are as easily produced as *p-n-p* types. Also, by this method, much closer control of the transistor characteristics is possible.

3 It follows from the above that a transistor can be considered as two junction diodes connected back to back as shown in *Fig 2*. For either of these arrangements

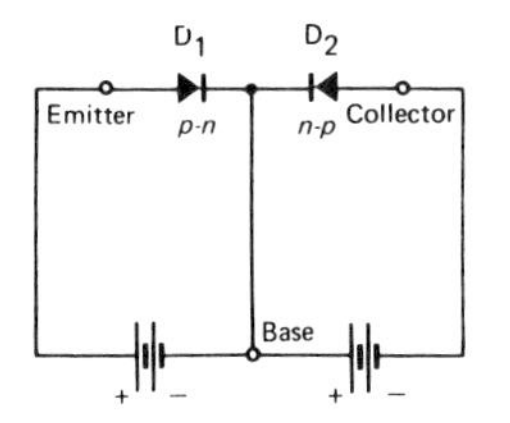

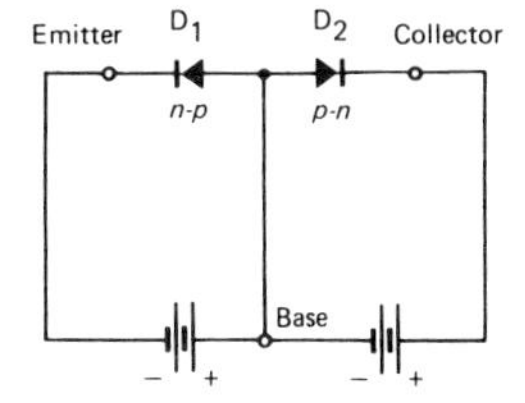

Fig 2

the three external connections are known as the **emitter**, **base** and **collector** connections. Batteries (or other forms of d.c. supply) are connected to these terminals in such a way that the emitter-base diode (D_1) is biased in the forward direction. This applied both to the *p-n-p* and the *n-p-n* arrangements; when the diodes are reversed, the respective battery polarities are also reversed.

The circuit properties of a transistor cannot be realised by using two discrete diodes as the diagram suggests. The construction of a sandwich of either *n-p-n* or *p-n-p* form, as already explained, effectively provides the two diode junctions in a single compact unit. A pictorial representation and the circuit symbols for both types of transistor are shown in *Fig 3*, where the arrowhead on the emitter indicates in both cases the *conventional* direction of current flow in the base-emitter diode. The direction of this arrow immediately distinguishes between a *p-n-p* or an *n-p-n* transistor.

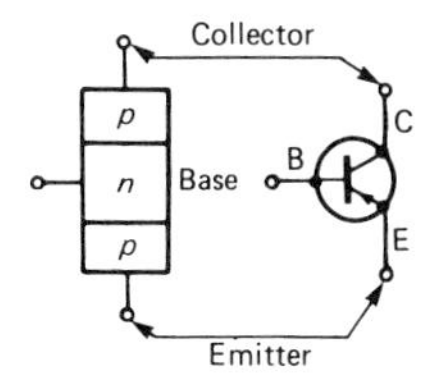

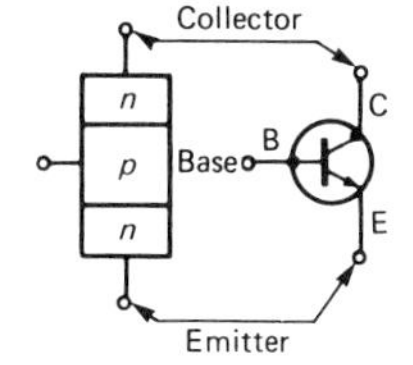

Fig 3

4 (i) In *Fig 4* where a representation of an *n-p-n* transistor is shown, consider what happens when the appropriate forward and reverse voltages are applied to the sandwich. In the forward-biased emitter-base diode, the majority carriers in the *n*-type emitter (electrons) are repelled from this region and flow across the junction into the base. In the base region the electrons drift towards the collector and are accepted by the collector which is biased positively with respect to the base.

It will be seen that electrons in the collector do not cross in any numbers into the base because the collector-base junction is reversed biased. Since the base is *p*-type material, electrons exist there only as minority carriers, so those electrons arriving at the collector are derived almost entirely from the emitter source.

On their way across the base a small proportion (about 0.1 to 0.5%) of the electrons recombine with the majority holes in the base and this loss of charge is made good by an *outward* flow of base current (as electrons) I_B. It is to reduce this 'loss' of electrons that the base wafer is made very thin, since the time spent by the electrons in crossing the base is then small and the possibility of recombination with holes is correspondingly reduced.

The effect as seen from the *external* circuit is that of a fairly large flow of current (electrons) into the emitter (I_E) and a small flow of electrons (I_B) out

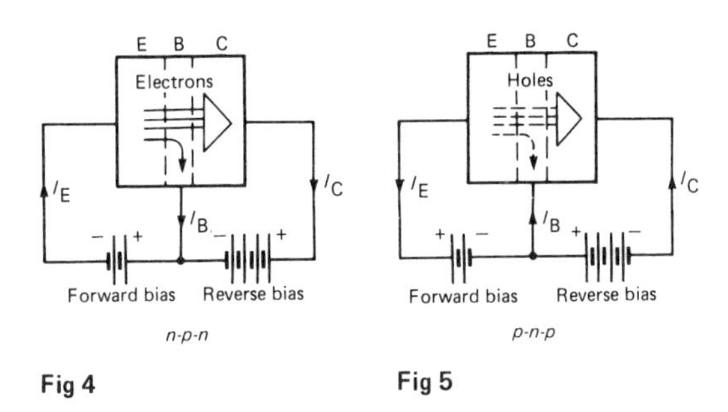

Fig 4 **Fig 5**

of the base. For a small general purpose transistor we might have such typical valves as 1 mA for I_E, 0.01 mA for I_B. Since the carriers originate at the emitter and distribute themselves between base and collector, the sum of the base and collector currents must always be equal to the emitter current, so that $I_E = I_B + I_C$.

(ii) The physical behaviour of the *p-n-p* transistor in *Fig 5* can be deduced in the same way. The majority carriers in the emitter region are holes, and these flow into the base when the base is biased negatively with respect to the emitter. The collector, which is now biased negatively with respect to the base, will absorb the holes, and a current will flow across the base-collector junction. Remember, only holes in the collector find this junction reverse biased. The result is that a large proportion of the holes flowing into the base cross the base wafer and appear at the collector.

Again, a few of the holes recombine with the majority electrons in the base and give rise to a small *inwards* flow of electrons into the base. Compare *Figs 4 and 5* carefully, noting the direction of movement of the electron or hole carriers inside the transistor and the corresponding movement of electron carriers only in the external circuit. Notice particularly that relative to the *n-p-n* transistor, the *p-n-p* circuit simply reverses both battery connections and the external current flow direction.

5 There are three possible ways in which a transistor can be connected into a practical circuit and these are shown in *Fig 6*. In all cases one terminal is common to what will be called the input and output ports, and the circuit **mode** or **configuration** is described in terms of this common terminal.

In *Fig 6*, (a) shows the common-base configuration, (b) the common-emitter configuration and (c) the common-collector configuration. The common terminal is

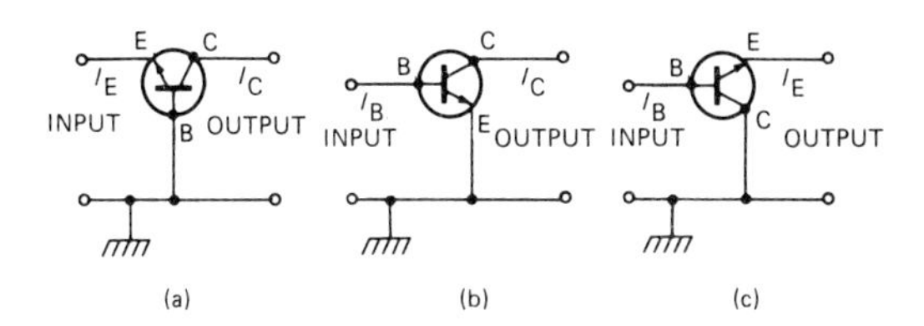

Fig 6

usually treated as being at earth potential and the term 'earthed' or 'grounded' instead of 'common' is sometimes used to describe the particular configuration. Diagram (a), for example, might well be referred to as the 'grounded base' connection.

6 Since the internal physical working of a transistor is unaffected by the form of configuration, the relationship between the input and output currents existing in each configuration can be readily deduced. Assuming that the appropriate battery supplies are connected to the transistor terminals, we may define the **static** current gain of the circuit as

$$\frac{\text{current flowing in the output circuit}}{\text{current flowing in the input circuit}}$$

The word 'static' is used here for the reason that the transistor is operating solely from direct current supplies (batteries), and no other external components or signals are involved. For the common-base configuration, the static current gain is designated the symbol α_B and is given by the ratio

$$\alpha_B = \frac{\text{collector current}}{\text{emitter current}} = \frac{I_C}{I_E}$$

since the base terminal is common.

In common-emitter configuration, current gain is designated α_E and is then given by the ratio

$$\alpha_E = \frac{\text{collector current}}{\text{base current}} = \frac{I_C}{I_B}$$

since the emitter terminal is common.

The symbols h_{FB} and h_{FE} are commonly used instead of α_B and α_E respectively for the static current gain, but these symbols will be explained in later work, and for the time being α_B and α_E will be employed.

Quite clearly, from a consideration of the way the current distributes itself inside a transistor

$$\alpha_B = \frac{I_C}{I_E} \text{ is always less than 1}$$

for the reason that I_C is always less than I_E

$$\alpha_E = \frac{I_C}{I_B} \text{ is always greater than 1}$$

for the reason that I_C is always greater than I_B

Because $I_E = I_C + I_B$ always, there is a relationship between α_B and α_E

$$\frac{\alpha_B}{\alpha_E} = \frac{I_B}{I_E} = \frac{I_E - I_C}{I_E} = 1 - \frac{I_C}{I_E} = 1 - \alpha_B$$

Therefore $\dfrac{\alpha_B}{\alpha_E} = 1 - \alpha_B$ or $\alpha_E = \dfrac{\alpha_B}{1 - \alpha_B}$

By transposition $\alpha_B = \dfrac{\alpha_E}{1 + \alpha_E}$

Also, the three currents I_E, I_C and I_B always flow in the ratio $1 : \alpha_B : 1 - \alpha_B$ whatever the configuration. These are important relationships.

7 The characteristics of a transistor, like any active device, are based on the input voltages and currents, the output voltages and currents and the relationships that exist between input and output variations of these.

Although a transistor is a three-terminal device, because one of these is always common to both input and output circuits, we may consider it as having a pair of input terminals and a pair of output terminals, see *Fig 7*. The characteristics can be displayed in graphical form showing the variations of input and output currents and voltages.

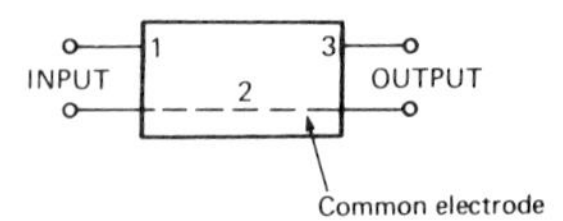

Fig 7

Although there are many possible characteristics, only four are of basic interest (two voltages and two currents), the others being particular cases of these four. Suitable circuits for the measurement of transistor characteristics are shown in *Fig 8*, diagram (a) being used for common-base measurements and (b) for common emitter. These are the more commonly used methods of connection. The transistors shown are *n-p-n* types, but equally *p-n-p* types could be substituted if the battery polarities were reversed. Notice that two voltmeters and two ammeters are used, since there are four variables involved, and two potentiometers P_1 and P_2 provide variable voltage supplies from batteries (or similar power units).

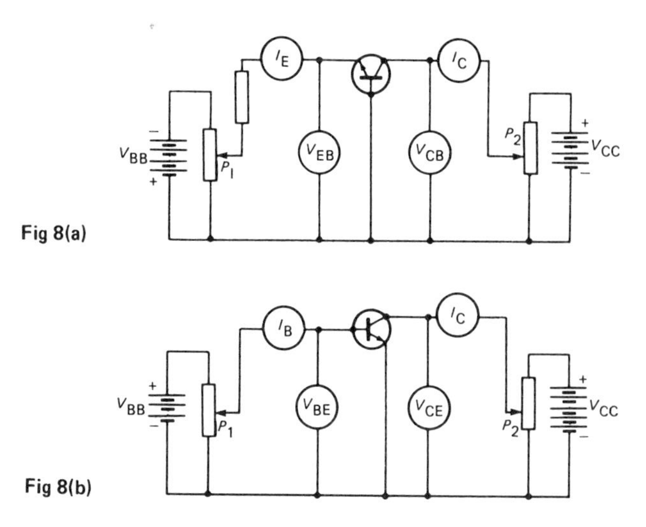

Fig 8(a)

Fig 8(b)

(a) Input characteristics

These characteristics relate only the input voltage and current variables. Hence, referring to *Fig 8*, only the voltmeter V_{BE} and ammeter I_E need be read. The collector voltage is set to its normal operating value and is *maintained* at that value while the input voltage is adjusted from zero to a few volts negative. The corresponding changes in the input current are observed. A graph is then drawn of input current (vertically) against input voltage (horizontally). As you might expect, since the base-emitter junction is essentially a forward biased diode, a characteristic similar in shape to that of a diode is obtained. Typical curves for both common-base and common-emitter are shown in *Fig 9*. These diagrams are called the input static characteristics. The position of the curve for both configuration shifts slightly if the collector voltage is changed to a new constant value but this can be ignored for most purposes.

The curves can be used to find the input resistance of the transistor. Both graphs give related values of I_E and V_{BE} for the common-base and of I_B and V_{BE} for the common-emitter connection. By selecting a point on either curve a pair of related values can be read off and by division V/I will give the usual Ohm's law value of resistance at *that* point. Since the curves are non-linear, the value for resistance obtained would be different at every point selected. Such a value would tell us the *static* input resistance. We are more concerned with the ratio

$$\frac{\text{the change in input voltage}}{\text{the change in input current}} = \frac{\delta V_{BE}}{\delta I_E}$$

because when a transistor is used as an amplifier, the input signal is not a d.c. level but an alternating quantity superimposed on a fixed d.c. level. The choice of the d.c. level depends upon the exact circuit requirements and once selected is known as the d.c. operating point. Such a point is indicated on the curves of *Fig 9* shown on the next page. The required ratio is then found as the *gradient* of the curve at point P. This value of input resistance is called the **dynamic** input resistance. It will not be the same as the value obtained for the static resistance at point P.

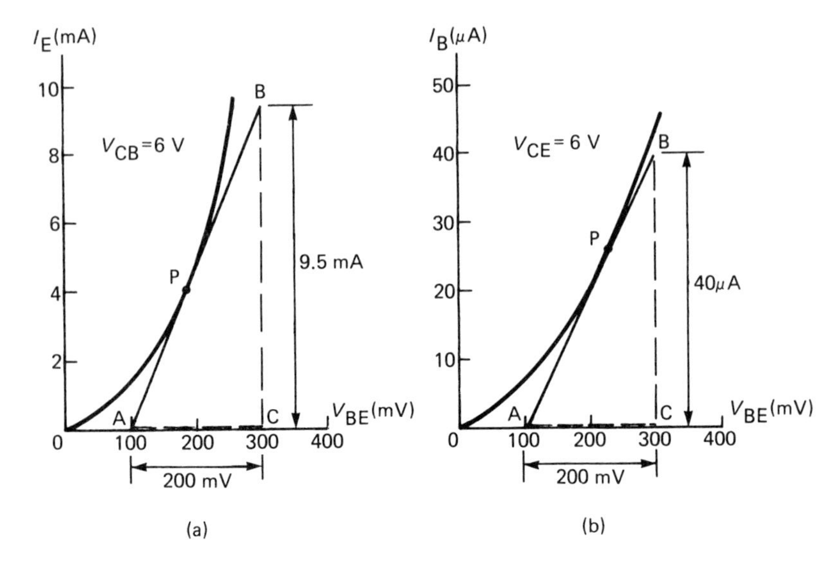

Fig 9

In *Fig 9(a)*

$$r_i = \frac{\text{AC (volts)}}{\text{BC (amps)}} = \frac{200 \times 10^{-3}}{9.5 \times 10^{-3}} = 21\ \Omega$$

and

In *Fig 9(b)*

$$r_i = \frac{\text{AC (volts)}}{\text{BC (amps)}} = \frac{200 \times 10^{-3}}{40 \times 10^{-6}} = 500\ \Omega$$

The input resistance of a common-base amplifier is always considerably *less* than that of a common-emitter.

(b) Output characteristics

Output characteristics are plots of collector current I_C against collector voltage V_{CE} for constant values of I_B in the case of common-emitter mode or I_E in the common-base mode. It is usual to draw a family of curves for each configuration over a range of fixed values for I_B or I_E.

The circuit of *Fig 8(a)* can be used to plot the output characteristics of the common-base mode. The first curve is plotted for zero input current, that is, for $I_E = 0$. The curve obtained is essentially that given by any reverse biased *p-n* junction and is shown appropriately marked in *Fig 10(a)*. I_E is now set to, say 2 mA by an adjustment of potentiometer P_1 and a second curve of I_C against V_{CB} obtained. This process is repeated for a number of different values of input current I_E; in the diagram these values are taken to be in 2 mA steps up to a maximum of 10 mA. Notice that for each setting of I_E the collector current is almost identical to I_E, the small difference in each case being the base current.

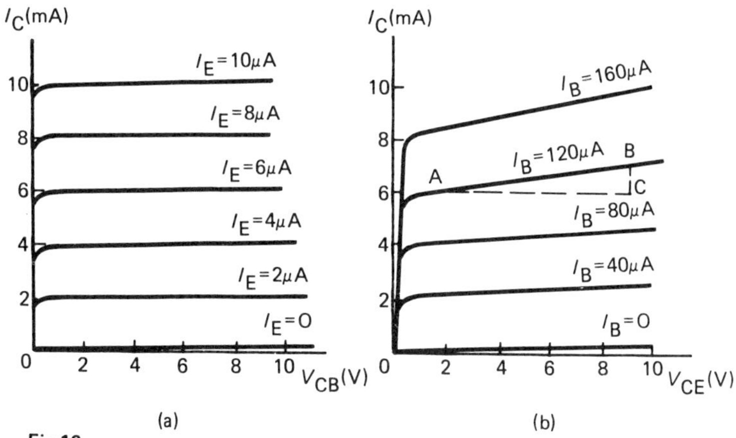

Fig 10

For the common-emitter configuration, the circuit of *Fig 8(b)* is used. The first curve is plotted for zero input current, that is, for $I_B = 0$. The collector current which then flows as V_{CE} is varied is due to the leakage current through the base-emitter junction, and this is shown appropriately marked in *Fig 10(b)*. I_B is now set to, say, 40 μA by an adjustment of potentiometer P_1 and a second curve of I_C against V_{CE} obtained. Again, a family of curves is obtained from the repeated process.

Looking at the curves of *Fig 10(a) and (b)* two points are observed:

(a) the characteristics, for values of V_{CE} above a fraction of a volt, are sensibly parallel to each other, the common-base configuration showing this best.

(b) the gradient of the characteristics is small (they are 'flat' curves), being rather greater in the case of the common-emitter configuration.

This shows that I_C is practically independent of the applied collector voltage which means that the transistors are behaving as sources of constant current.

The curves can be used to find the output resistance of the transistor. We should expect this to be large because we are 'looking' into a reverse biased diode. The simple ratio V_{CE}/I_C at any point on the curves for common-emitter would give us the resistance of the collector-base junction but we require the dynamic output resistance. This is found from the gradient of the graph as the ratio:

$$\frac{\text{the change in output voltage}}{\text{the change in output current}} = \frac{\delta V_{CE}}{\delta I_C}$$

In *Fig 11*, the triangle ABC is drawn on the appropriate characteristic. Then

$$\text{output resistance } r_o = \frac{\text{AC (volts)}}{\text{BC (amperes)}} \ \Omega$$

As the characteristics are almost straight lines, the value of r_o is practically constant over quite wide variations of collector voltage.

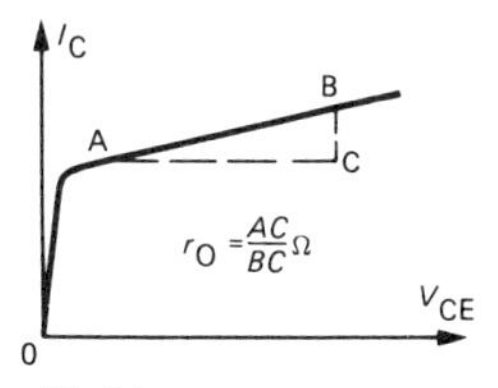

Fig 11

B. WORKED PROBLEMS ON BIPOLAR TRANSISTORS AND THEIR CHARACTERISTICS

Problem 1 Describe the effect of the leakage current which flows across the reverse biased collector-base junction of a transistor.

For an *n-p-n* transistor, the reverse-biased base-collector junction behaves as a diode and a small leakage current, designated I_{CBO}, flows from the collector to the base. This current is due to the movement of minority carriers across the junction (holes in the collector and electrons in the base). But a movement of holes from collector to base is equivalent to a movement of electrons in the direction base-to-collector.

Hence, in the external circuit the leakage current flows in the *same* direction as that due to the collected electrons, the majority carriers. If a proportion, α, of the electrons passing from the emitter to the base also pass from the base to the collector, then the currents flowing in an *n-p-n* transistor are as shown in *Fig 12(a)*. You should compare this diagram with *Fig 4*, earlier in this chapter, where the leakage current was ignored.

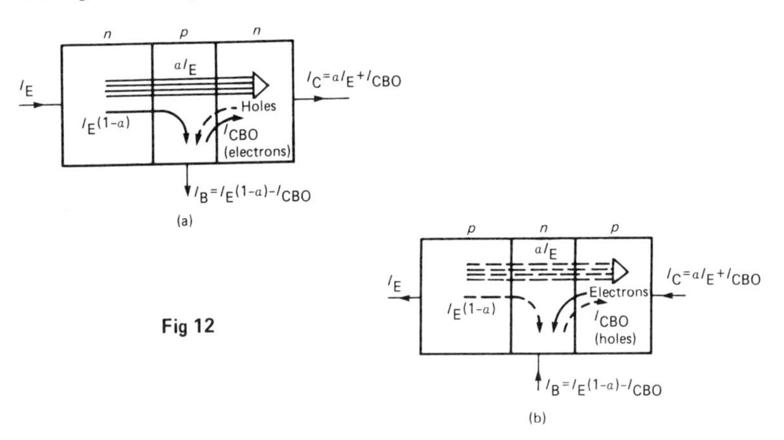

Fig 12

Similarly, for a *p-n-p* transistor, the base-collector junction is reverse biased for majority carriers (holes) but a small leakage current I_{CBO} flows from the collector to the base due to the movement of minority carriers across the junction (electrons in the collector and holes in the base). Again this leakage current flows in the external circuit in the same direction as that due to the collected holes, the majority carriers. The currents flowing in a *p-n-p* transistor are shown in *Fig 12(b)*.

Problem 2 Deduce the static current gain of the common collector configuration in terms of α_E.

In the common-collector configuration, the input is applied between base and collector; see *Fig 6(c)*. Hence we treat I_B as input current and I_E as output current. The current gain is therefore

$$\alpha_C = \frac{I_E}{I_B}$$

This ratio is clearly very much greater than 1.
Since $I_E = I_C + I_B$, we can write

$$\alpha_C = \frac{I_C + I_B}{I_B} = \frac{I_C}{I_B} + 1$$

But $\frac{I_C}{I_B} = \alpha_E$, the common-emitter static current gain

Hence

$$\alpha_C = \alpha_E + 1$$

Problem 3 Explain why the output characteristic curves of both common-base and common-emitter modes are practically horizontal lines. In the case of common-base mode, explain why collector current flows even when the collector voltage is reduced to zero; see *Fig 10(a)*.

Since the curves are practically horizontal, the collector current must be substantially independent of collector voltage. This is because collector current is derived from the charge carriers originating in the emitter. On entering the base these carriers are almost entirely gathered up by the collector, even if the collector-to-base voltage is very small. Increases in the collector voltage will have little effect on the collector current because it is not the collector voltage which is producing the carriers. The horizontal portions of the curves where practically all the emitted carriers are being taken by the collector are known as the **current saturation** regions.

Looking at the curves of *Fig 10(a)*, if V_{CB} is reduced to zero collector current still flows because the collector is able to gather carriers (electrons in this case) from the base due to the presence of the junction p.d. developed across the depletion layer. A reversed V_{CB} of a fraction of a volt is necessary therefore to reduce I_C to zero.

Problem 4 The data given in the following table refer to a transistor in common-emitter configuration. Plot the output characteristic curves.

	I_C (mA)		
V_{CE}	$I_B = 20\ \mu A$	$I_B = 60\ \mu A$	$I_B = 100\ \mu A$
2	1.6	3.5	5.7
6	1.8	3.95	6.4
10	2.0	4.3	7.0

From the curves estimate (a) the output resistance for $I_B = 60\ \mu A$;
(b) the static current gain α_E for $V_{CE} = 6$ V, $I_B = 60\ \mu A$.

The required curves are shown in *Fig 13*. Notice how the collector current values are plotted against the given values of collector voltage for each of the three values of base current.

The output resistance, measured from the $I_B = 60\ \mu A$ characteristic, is obtained by

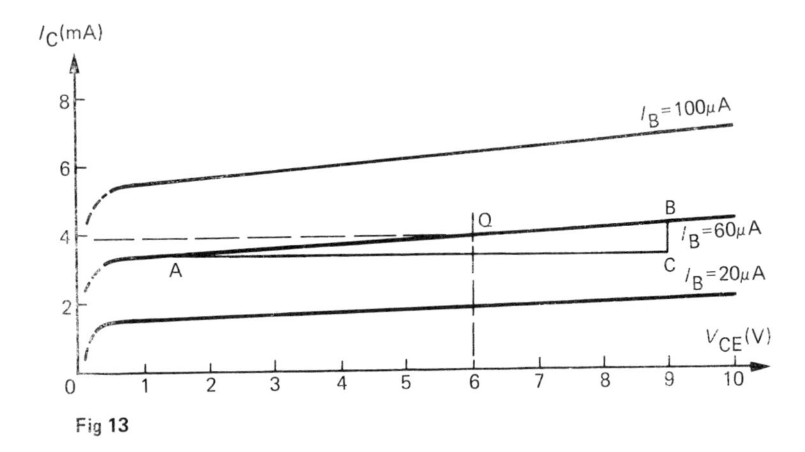

Fig 13

drawing the triangle ABC. Note the size of this triangle; a small triangle does not give accurate results. Now AC = 8 V, BC = 0.75 mA. Hence

$$\text{output resistance } r_o = \frac{AC}{BC} = \frac{8}{0.75 \times 10^{-3}} = 10667\ \Omega$$

To obtain the static current gain α_E we must make use of the ratio representing this gain, that is

$$\alpha_E = \frac{I_C}{I_B}$$

For $V_{CE} = 6$ V and $I_B = 60$ μA this condition is given by the point marked Q. At this point, $I_B = 60$ μA $I_C = 3.95$ mA. Hence

$$\alpha_E = \frac{3.95 \text{ mA}}{60\ \mu\text{A}} = 65.8$$

We shall see in due course that this static gain is usually greater than the dynamic gain obtained under signal conditions.

Problem 5 Explain what is meant by the transfer characteristic and show how it can be derived from the output characteristics.

The transfer characteristic is a graph which shows the influence of the input current upon the output current for a specified value of collector voltage. If the collector voltage is maintained at a constant value and the input current is varied (by adjustment of the input voltage), the simultaneous changes in collector current and emitter (for common-base) or base (for common-emitter) current may be recorded. When output current is plotted against input current, a practically straight line results; see *Fig 14(a) and (b)*. The gradient of this line gives the value of α_B (diagram (a)) or α_E (diagram (b)).

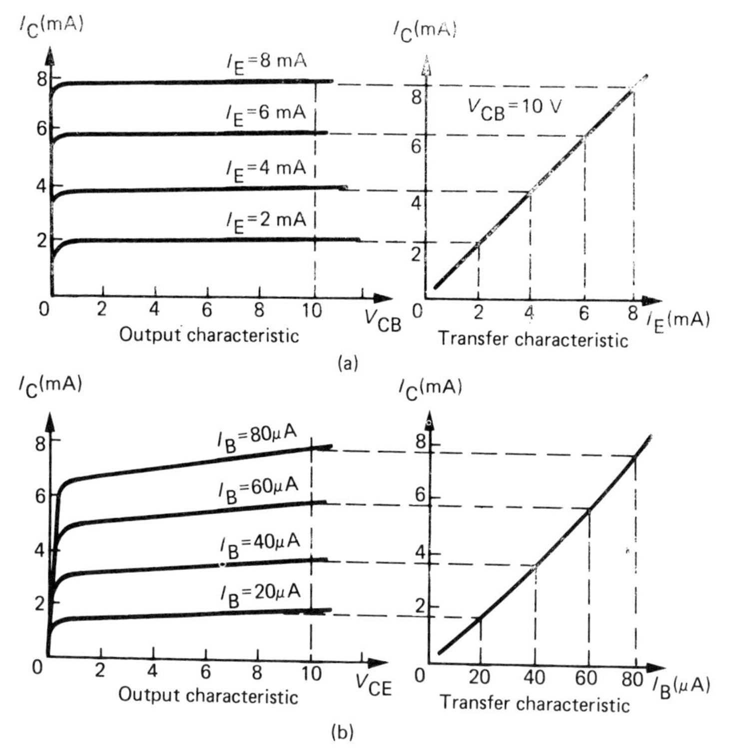

Fig 14

The characteristic for common-base is more linear than that for common-emitter. Since $I_E = I_B + I_C$ and I_C is plotted against I_E in diagram (a), the gradient of the line is only slightly less than 45°. Since tan 45° = 1, $I_E \simeq I_C$.

The figures show how the transfer chracteristics are obtained from the respective output characteristics for a given values of V_{CE}.

C. FURTHER PROBLEMS ON BIPOLAR TRANSISTORS AND THEIR CHARACTERISTICS

(a) SHORT ANSWER PROBLEMS (answers on page 133)

1 Complete the following: (more than one word may be needed)
   (a) In any transistor, the emitter-base junction is .... biased and the collector-base junction is .... biased.
   (b) An *n-p-n* transisor requires the collector polarity to be ....
   (c) The arrow on the emitter of a *p-n-p* transistor points .... the base

(d) In the common-emitter configuration, the input terminals are the . . . . and emitter and the output terminals are the . . . . and emitter.
(e) $I_E - I_B$ is always equal to . . . .
(f) The static current gain of the common . . . . configuration is always greater than unity.
(g) The carriers crossing the base of an *n-p-n* transistor are . . . .
(h) Recombination of electrons with holes in the base of an *n-p-n* transistor causes an electron flow . . . . the base terminal.
(j) If a transistor existed in which no carriers were lost in base recombination its common-base static current gain would be . . . .

2 A transistor has an emitter current of 2 mA and a collector current of 1.975 mA. What is its base current?

3 For the transistor of the previous problem, what would be its static current gain for (i) common-base; (ii) common emitter configuration?

4 A transistor has a common-emitter current gain of 200. What will be its gain in common-base?

5 The common-base gain of a transistor is 0.985. What is its gain in common-emitter?

6 Say whether the following statements are true or false:

(a) $\alpha_E = \dfrac{\alpha_B}{1 + \alpha_B}$
(b) A transistor can be connected into a circuit in one of three possible ways.
(c) The operation of a transistor depends upon which configuration it is in.
(d) In common-base configuration the output signal is taken from between collector and base.
(e) The input resistance of common-base is much greater than that of common-emitter.
(f) Input resistance does not change significantly with collector voltage.
(g) If α_E is known, α_B can be calculated.
(h) The static current gain of a transistor can be obtained from the output characteristics.
(j) The number of majority carriers entering the base from the emitter depends upon the collector voltage.
(k) In common-emitter mode, a small collector current flows when the base is disconnected.
(l) The polarity of the collector has to be opposite to that of the carriers crossing into the base from the emitter.

(b) CONVENTIONAL PROBLEMS

1 A transistor in common-emitter mode has a base current of 100 μA with a bias voltage of 1.0 V. A change in input signal of 0.1 V causes the base current to rise to 125 μA. What are the values of the static and the dynamic input resistance?
[10 kΩ; 4 kΩ]

2 If I_C = 4.0 mA when V_{CE} = 2.0 V, and 5.0 mA when 8.0 V, I_B being held constant, calculate the dynamic output resistance under this condition.
[6 kΩ]

3 If $I_C = 5.0$ mA when $V_{CB} = 8.0$ V, and 5.02 mA when 12 V, I_E being held constant, estimate the output resistance under this condition.

[200 kΩ]

4 In a common-base configuration, with V_{CB} held constant, V_{EB} is 120 mV when I_E is 1.0 mA and 200 mV when 7.0 mA. What is the dynamic input resistance of the transistor?

[13.34 Ω]

5 The table gives the input characteristic parameters of a germanium transistor in common-emitter mode, for V_{CE} held at 4.5 V.

V_{BE}	75	100	125	150	175	200	(mV)
I_B	3	8	20	40	72	100	μA

Plot the input characteristic carefully, and from it evaluate the static and dynamic input resistance when $I_B = 40$ μA.

6 With the aid of a circuit diagram, explain how the input, output and transfer characteristics of an *n-p-n* transistor connected in common-base mode can be obtained.

7 Describe the principle of operation of a bipolar transistor, explaining particularly why majority carriers entering the base from the emitter are gathered by the collector and why the collector current is substantially independent of collector voltage.

8 What effect does leakage current have on the normal collector current of a transistor connected in (a) common-emitter; (b) common-base. Consider both *p-n-p* and *n-p-n* transistors.

9 The following table refers to a transistor connected in common-emitter mode.

	I_C (mA)			
V_{CE}	$I_B = 20$ μA	40 μA	60 μA	80 μA
3	0.91	1.60	2.30	3.0
5	0.93	1.70	2.50	3.25
7	0.97	1.85	2.70	3.55
9	0.99	2.04	3.0	4.05

Plot the output characteristics for the given range of base currents and use the curves to determine (a) the output resistance when $I_B = 60$ μA; (b) the current gain α_E when $V_{CE} = 6$ V.

[(a) 8570 Ω; (b) 42]

5 Small signal amplifiers

A. MAIN POINTS CONCERNING SMALL SIGNAL AMPLIFIERS

1 The amplifying properties of a transistor depend upon the fact that current flowing in a low-resistance circuit is transferred to a high-resistance circuit with negligible change in magnitude. If the current is then caused to flow through a load resistor, a voltage is developed. This voltage can be many times greater than the input voltage which caused the original current flow.

The basic circuit for a transistor is illustrated in *Fig 1*. Here an *n-p-n* transistor is biased in the manner previously described with batteries B_1 and B_2. An input alternating signal, v_e assumed to be sinusoidal, is placed in series with the input bias voltage, and a load resistor, R_L, is placed in series with the collector bias voltage. The input signal is therefore the sinusoidal current i_e resulting from the application of the sinusoidal voltage v_e, **superimposed** on the direct current I_E established by the base-emitter voltage V_{BE}.

Suppose the signal voltage v_e is 100 mV and this flows in a base-emitter circuit resistance of 50 Ω. Then the emitter signal current will be 2 mA. If the load resistance is 3 kΩ, then about 0.99 of the emitter current will flow in it. Hence the collector signal current will be about $0.99 \times 2 = 1.98$ mA and the signal voltage across the load will be $3000 \times 1.98 \times 10^{-3} = 5.94$ V. Thus a signal voltage of 100 mV at the emitter has produced a voltage of 5940 mV across the load. The voltage amplification or gain is therefore $5940/100 = 59.4$ times.

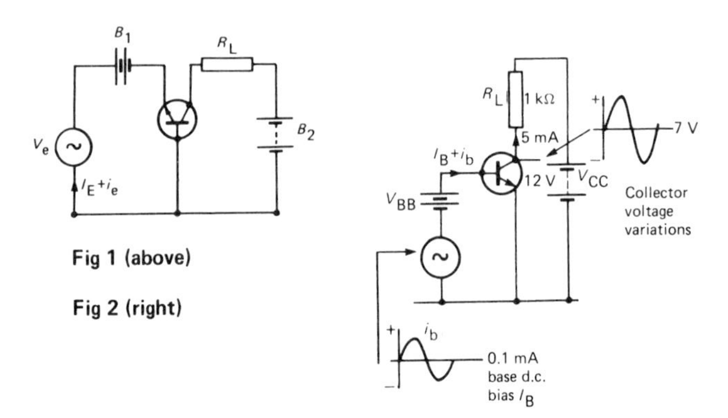

Fig 1 (above)

Fig 2 (right)

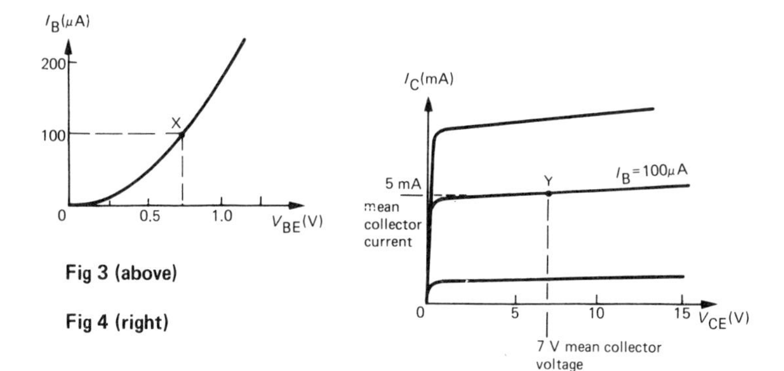

Fig 3 (above)

Fig 4 (right)

2 This example illustrates the action of a common-base amplifier. The input signal is applied between emitter and base and the output is taken from between collector and base. We shall now deal with the **common-emitter amplifier**. The basic circuit arrangement is shown in *Fig 2*. Although two batteries are shown, it is more usual to employ only one to supply all the necessary bias. The input signal is now applied between base and emitter, and the load resistor R_L is connected between collector and emitter. Suppose, by way of example, that the base bias battery provides a voltage such that it causes a base current $I_B = 0.1$ mA to flow. Again, this value of base current determines the mean d.c. level upon which the a.c. input signal will be superimposed. This is the **d.c. base current operating point**.

Let the static current gain of the transistor, a_E, be 50. Since 0.1 mA is the steady base current, the collector current I_C will be $\alpha_E I_B = 50 \times 0.1 = 5$ mA. This current will flow through the load resistor R_L, taken here to be 1 kΩ, and there will be a steady voltage drop across R_L given by $I_C R_L = 5 \times 10^{-3} \times 1000 = 5$ V. The voltage at the collector will therefore be $V_{CC} - I_C R_L = 12 - 5 = 7$ V. This value of V_{CE} is the mean (or **quiescent**) level about which the output signal voltage will swing alternately positive and negative. This is the **collector voltage d.c. operating point**.

3 Both of these d.c. operating points can be pin-pointed on the input and output characteristics of the transistor. *Fig 3* shows the $I_B - V_{BE}$ characteristics with the operating point X positioned at $I_B = 0.1$ mA, $V_{BE} = 0.75$ V, say.

Fig 4 shows the $I_C - V_{CE}$ characteristics, with the operating point Y positioned at $I_C = 5$ mA, $V_{CE} = 7$ V. It is usual to choose the operating points Y somewhere near the centre of the graph.

It is possible to get rid of the bias battery V_{BB} and obtain base bias from the collector supply battery V_{CC} instead. The simplest way to do this is to connect a bias resistor R_B between the positive terminal of the V_{CC} supply and the base as shown in *Fig 5*. The resistor must be of such a value that it allows 0.1 mA to flow in the base-emitter diode.

For a silicon transistor, the voltage drop across the junction for forward bias conditions is about 0.6 V. The voltage across R_B must then be $12 - 0.6 = 11.4$ V. Hence, the value of R_B must be such that $I_B . R_B = 11.4$ V. From this, for $I_B = 0.1$ mA, $R_B = 114$ kΩ. With the inclusion of the 1 kΩ load resistor, a steady 5 mA collector current, and a collector-emitter voltage of 7 V, the d.c. conditions are established.

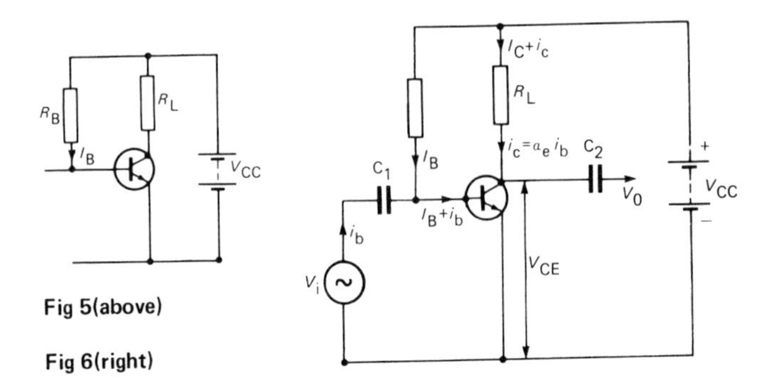

Fig 5(above)

Fig 6(right)

An alternating input signal (v_i) can now be applied. In order not to disturb the bias condition established at the base, the input must be fed to the base by way of a capacitor C_1. This will permit the alternating signal to pass to the base but will prevent the passage of direct current. The reactance of this capacitor must be such that it is very small compared with the input resistance of the transistor. The circuit of the amplifier has now developed to that shown in *Fig 6*. The a.c. conditions can now be followed through.

4 When an alternating signal voltage v_i is applied to the base via capacitor C_1 the base current i_b varies. When the input signal swings positive, the base current increases; when the signal swings negative, the base current decreases. The base current consists of two components: I_B, the static base bias established by R_B plus i_b, the signal current. The current variation i_b will in turn vary the collector current, i_c. The relationship between i_c and i_b is given by α_e, so that $i_c = \alpha_e i_b$. This α_e is the **dynamic** current gain of the transistor and is not quite the same as the static current gain α_E covered earlier. The difference is generally small enough not to be significant.

The current through the load resistor R_L also consists of two components: I_C, the static collector current plus i_c, the signal current. As i_b increases, so does i_c and so does the voltage drop across R_L. Hence, from the circuit

$$V_{CE} = V_{CC} - (I_C + i_c) R_L$$

The d.c. components of this equation, though necessary for the amplifier to operate at all, need not be considered when the a.c. signal conditions are being examined. Hence, the signal voltage variation relationship is:

$$v_{ce} = -\alpha_e . i_b . R_L = i_c R_L$$

the negative sign being added because v_{ce} decreases when i_b increases and vice versa. So the signal output and input voltages are of opposite polarity or a phase shift of 180° has occurred. So that the collector d.c. potential is not passed on to the following stage, a second capacitor (C_2) is added as shown in *Fig 6*. This removes the direct component but permits the signal voltage $v_o = i_c R_L$ to pass to the output terminals.

5 The relationship between the collector-emitter voltage (V_{CE}) and collector current (I_C) is given by the equation

$$V_{CE} = V_{CC} - I_C R_L$$

in terms of the **d.c. conditions.** Since V_{CC} and R_L are constant in any given circuit, this represents the equation of a straight line which can be written in the $y = mx + c$ form

$$I_C = -\frac{1}{R_L} V_{CE} + \frac{V_{CC}}{R_L}$$

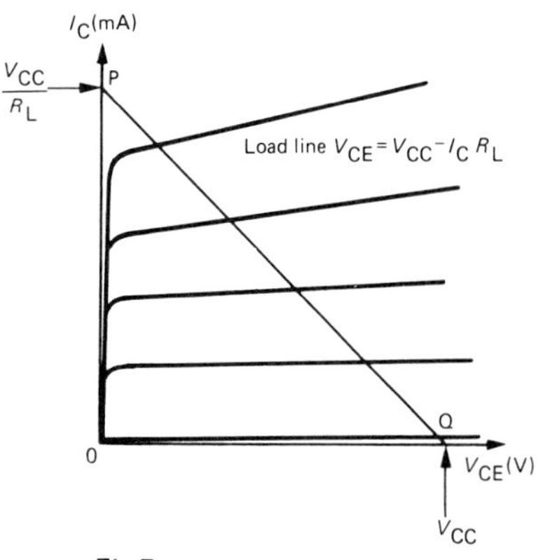

Fig 7

The gradient of the line is $-1/R_L$ and the vertical intercept is V_{CC}/R_L. Thus a straight line may be drawn on the co-ordinate axes of I_C against V_{CE}. But we already have a family of collector static characteristics drawn on these axes *Fig 10(b)* on page 41 and so the line may be superimposed on these, see *Fig 7.*

The reason why this line is necessary is because the static curves relate I_C to V_{CE} for a series of *fixed* values of I_B. When a signal is applied to the base of the transistor, the base current varies and can instantaneously take any of the values between the extremes shown. Only two points are necessary to draw the line and these can be found conveniently by considering extreme conditions. From the equation

$$V_{CE} = V_{CC} - I_C R_L$$

(i) when $I_C = 0$ $V_{CE} = V_{CC}$

(ii) when $V_{CE} = 0$ $I_C = \frac{V_{CC}}{R_L}$

Thus the points Q and P respectively are located on the axes of the $I_C - V_{CE}$ characteristics. This line is called the **load line** and it is dependent for its position upon the value of V_{CC} and for its gradient upon R_L. As the gradient is given by $-1/R_L$, the slope of the line is negative, that is, it slopes 'backwards'.

For every value assigned to R_L in a particular circuit there will be a corresponding (and different) load line. If V_{CC} is maintained constant, all the possible lines will start at the same point (Q) but will cut the I_C axis at different points P. Increasing R_L will reduce the gradient of the line and vice-versa. Quite clearly the collector voltage can never exceed V_{CC} (point Q) and equally the collector current can never be greater than that value which would make V_{CE} zero (point P).

Using the circuit example of *Fig 2* we have

$$V_{CE} = V_{CC} = 12 \text{ V, when } I_C = 0$$

$$I_C = \frac{V_{CC}}{R_L} = \frac{12}{1000} \text{ A} = 12 \text{ mA, when } V_{CE} = 0$$

The load line is drawn on the characteristics shown in *Fig 8* which we assume are the characteristics for the transistor used in the circuit of *Fig 2* earlier. Notice that the load line passes through the operating point X as it should, since every position on the line represents a relationship between V_{CE} and I_C for the particular values of V_{CC} and R_L given. Suppose that the base current is caused to vary ± 0.1 mA about the d.c. base bias of 0.1 mA. The result is I_B changes from 0 mA to 0.2 mA and back again to 0 mA during the course of each input cycle. Hence the operating point moves up and down the load line in phase with the input current and hence the input voltage. A sinusoidal input cycle is shown on *Fig 8*.

The output signal voltage (v_{ce}) and current (i_c) can be obtained by projecting vertically from the load line on to V_{CE} and I_C axes respectively. When the input current i_b varies sinusoidally as shown, then v_{ce} varies sinusoidally if the points A and B at the extremities of the input excursions are equally spaced on either side of X.

The peak to peak output voltage is seen to be 8.5 V, giving an r.m.s. value of 3 V. The peak to peak output current is 8.75 mA, giving an r.m.s. value of 3.1 mA. From these figures the voltage and current amplifications can be obtained.

6 The dynamic current gain A_i ($= \alpha_e$) as opposed to the static gain α_E, is expressed as

$$A_i = \frac{\text{the change in collector current}}{\text{the change in base current}}$$

This always leads to a different figure from that obtained by the direct division of

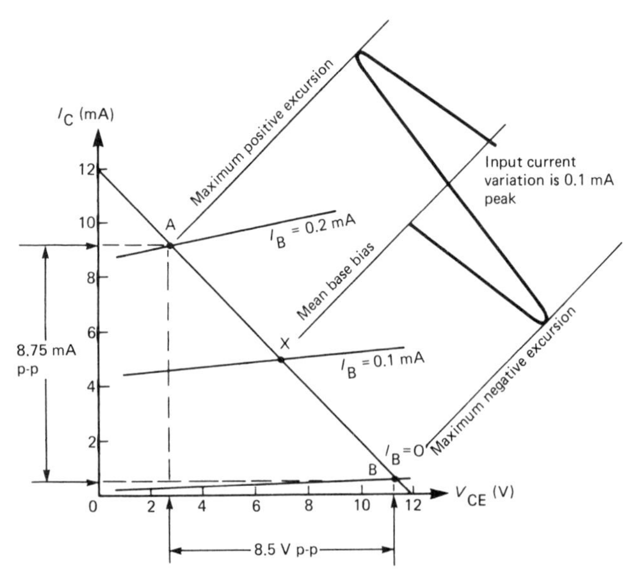

Fig 8

I_C/I_B which assumes that the collector load resistor is zero. From *Fig 8* the peak input current is 100 μA and the peak output current is 4.375 mA. Hence

$$A_i = \frac{4.375 \times 10^{-3}}{100 \times 10^{-6}} = 43.75$$

The voltage gain A_V is obtained from the ratio

$$A_V = \frac{\text{the change in collector voltage}}{\text{the change in base voltage}}$$

We cannot calculate this from the data available, but if we assume that the base current flows in the input resistance, then the base voltage can be found. The input resistance can be found from an input characteristic such as was shown in *Fig 9* earlier.

Then

$$R_i = \frac{\text{change in } V_{BC}}{\text{change in } I_B}$$

and

$$v_i = i_b R_c \text{ and } v_o = i_c R_L \text{ and}$$

$$A_V = \frac{i_c R_L}{i_b R_i} = \alpha_e \frac{R_L}{R_i}$$

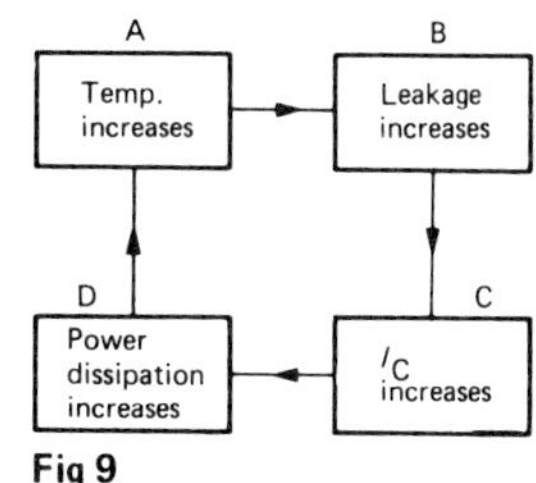

Fig 9

7 When a transistor is used as an amplifier (or indeed for any purpose) it is necessary to ensure that it does not overheat. Overheating can arise from causes outside of the transistor itself, such as the proximity of radiators or hot resistors, or within the transistor as the result of power dissipation by the passage of current through it. Power dissipated within the transistor which is given approximately by the product $I_C \cdot V_{CE}$ is wasted power; it contributes nothing to the signal output power and merely raises the temperature of the transistor. Such overheating can lead to very undesirable results.

In *Fig 9*, suppose that an increase in the temperature of the transistor is represented by box A. This increase will give rise to the production of hole-electron pairs, hence an increase in leakage current represented by the additional minority carriers, box B. In turn, this leakage current leads to an increase in collector current, as at box C, and this increases the product $I_C V_{CE}$. Hence the temperature rise already present in box A is enhanced by the additional power output from box D. The whole effect thus becomes self sustaining and results in **thermal runaway**. This rapidly leads to the destruction of the transistor.

B. WORKED PROBLEMS ON SMALL SIGNAL AMPLIFIERS

Problem 1 Explain how thermal runaway might be prevented in a transistor.

Two basic approaches are available and either or both may be used in a particular application. One approach is in the circuit design itself. The use of a single biasing resistor R_B as shown earlier in *Fig 5* is not particularly good practice. If the temperature of the transistor increases, the leakage current also increases. The collector current, collector voltage and base current are thereby changed, the base current decreasing as I_C increases. An alternative is shown in *Fig 10*. Here the resistor R_B is returned, not to the V_{CC} line, but to the collector itself.

If the collector current increases for any reason, the collector voltage V_{CE} will fall. Therefore, the d.c. base current I_B will fall, since $I_B = V_{CE}/R_B$. Hence the collector current $I_C = \alpha_E I_B$ will also fall and compensate for the original increase.

A commonly used bias arrangement is shown in *Fig 11*. If the total resistance value

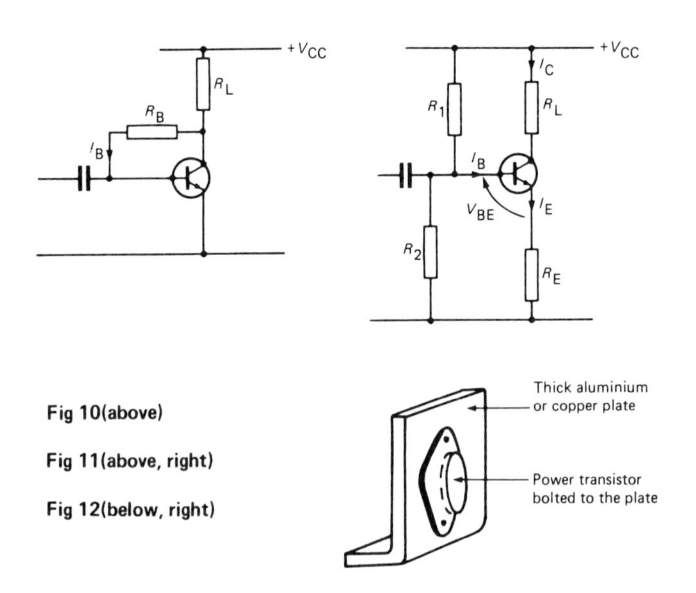

Fig 10(above)

Fig 11(above, right)

Fig 12(below, right)

of resistors R_1 and R_2 is such that the current flowing through the divider is large compared with the d.c. bias current I_B, then the base voltage V_{BE} will remain substantially constant regardless of variations in collector current. The emitter resistor R_E in turn determines the value of emitter current which flows for a given base voltage at the junction of R_1 and R_2. Any increase in I_C produces an increase in I_E and a corresponding increase in the voltage drop across R_E. This reduces the forward bias voltage V_{BE} and leads to a compensating reduction in I_C.

A second approach concerns some means of keeping the transistor temperature down by external cooling. For this purpose, a heat sink is employed, *Fig 12*. If the transistor is clipped or bolted to a large conducting area of aluminium or copper plate (which may have cooling fins), cooling is achieved by convection and radiation.

Heat sinks are usually blackened to assist radiation and are normally used where large power dissipations are involved. With small transistors, heat sinks are unnecessary. Silicon transistors particularly have such small leakage currents that thermal problems rarely arise.

Problem 2 An *n-p-n* transistor has the following characteristics which may be assumed to be linear (straight) between the values of collector voltage stated.

Base current (μA)	*Collector current (mA) for collector voltages of* 1 V	5 V
30	1.4	1.6
50	3.0	3.5
70	4.6	5.2

The transistor is used as a common-emitter amplifier with load resistor $R_C = 1.2$ kΩ and a collector supply of 7 V. The signal input resistance is 1 kΩ. Estimate the voltage gain A_v, the current gain A_i and the power gain A_p when an input current of 20 μA peak varies sinusoidally about a mean bias of 50 μA.

The characteristics are drawn in *Fig 13*. The load line equation is $V_{CC} = V_{CE} + I_C R_L$ which enables the extreme points of the line to be calculated. When $I_C = 0$, $V_{CE} = V_C = 7.0$ V; when $V_{CE} = 0$, $I_C = V_{CC}/R_L = 7/1200 = 5.83$ mA. The load line is shown superimposed on the characteristic curves with the operating point marked X at the intersection of the line and the 50 μA characteristic.

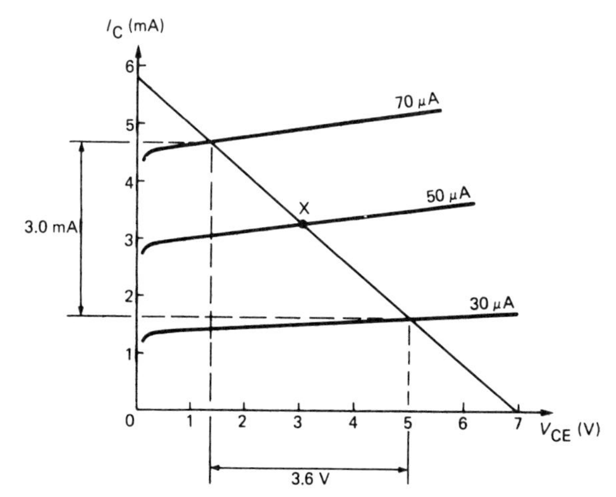

Fig 13

From the diagram, the output voltage swing is 3.6 V peak to peak. The input voltage swing is $i_b R_i$ where i_b is the base current swing and R_i is the input resistance. Therefore

$$v_i = 40 \times 10^{-6} \times 1 \times 10^3 = 40 \text{ mV peak to peak}$$

Therefore

$$A_V = \frac{\text{output volts}}{\text{input volts}} = \frac{3.6}{40 \times 10^{-3}} = 90$$

Note that peak to peak values are taken at both input and output. There is no need to convert to r.m.s. as only ratios are involved.

From the diagram, the output current swing is 3.0 mA peak to peak. The input base current swing is 40 μA peak to peak. Therefore

$$A_i = \frac{\text{output current}}{\text{input current}} = \frac{3 \times 10^{-3}}{40 \times 10^{-6}} = 75$$

For a resistance load R_L the power gain is simply

$$A_p = \text{voltage gain} \times \text{current gain} = A_V . A_i = 90 \times 75 = 6750$$

Problem 3 The common-emitter amplifier of *Fig 14* has a 10 V supply and requires a d.c. bias current of 50 μA corresponding to a base emitter voltage of 0.6 V for stability reasons the current through R_1 is ten times the base current. Assess suitable values for R_1, R_2, R_E and R_L.

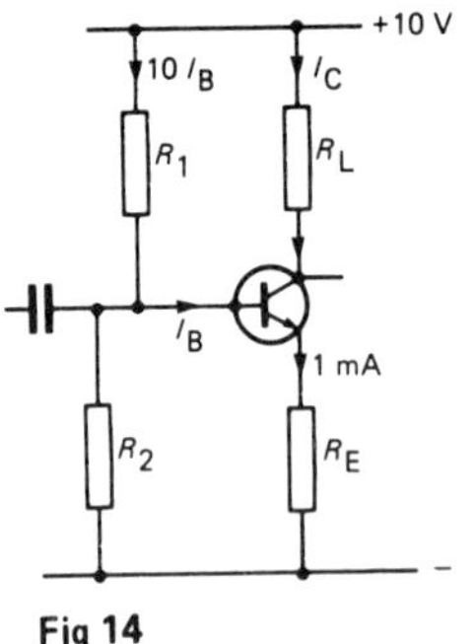

Fig 14

The emitter current is indicated as 1 mA. Let the voltage drop across R_E be 1 V, a typical value in this kind of circuit. Then

$$R_E = \frac{1}{10^{-3}} = 1 \text{ k}\Omega$$

The current through R_1 is 10 I_B or 0.5 mA. Hence the current through R_2 will be 9 I_B. The p.d. across $R_2 = V_{BE} + I_E R_E = 0.6 + 1.0 = 1.6$ V. But at a current of 9 I_B = 0.45 mA, the p.d. across $R_2 = 0.45 R_2$.

Therefore

$$0.45R_2 = 1.6 \text{ V}. R_2 = \frac{1.6}{0.45} \times 10^3 = 3.6 \text{ k}\Omega$$

The voltage across

$$R_1 = 10 - 1.6 = 8.4 \text{ V. Therefore } R_1 = \frac{8.4}{0.5} \times 10^3 = 16.8 \text{ k}\Omega$$

Since there is a 1 V drop across R_E, 9 V is available for R_L and V_{CE}. This may be divided equally so giving a mean collector voltage of 4.5 V. Hence as $I_C \simeq I_E$

$$R_L = \frac{4.5}{1} \times 10^3 = 4.5 \text{ k}\Omega.$$

Problem 4 Explain how leakage current inside the transistor affects the current flowing in the external circuit. Why is leakage current of more importance in the common emitter circuit than in common-base?

Fig 15 shows an *n-p-n* transistor connected to collector and base bias supplies but with the emitter disconnected. It might appear that under this condition I_C would be zero since clearly I_E is zero. However, the collector-base diode is reverse biased by the total effective voltage acting in the circuit and this diode must pass reverse or leakage current.

This current is due to the movement of minority charge carriers (holes in the *n-p-n* transistor) across the junction in the direction collector-to-base. But such a movement of holes from collector-to-base inside the transistor is equivalent to a movement of electrons in the direction base-to-collector.

Hence in the *external* circuit the leakage current flows in the same direction as that due to the collected electrons, the majority carriers. This leakage current is denoted by I_{CBO}, the flow being across the collector-base junction with the emitter disconnected. This current still flows when the emitter is reconnected and the main forward current from the emitter is superimposed. So far we have assumed the collector current in common-base to be $\alpha_B I_E$. But with the addition of the leakage component, the collector current becomes $I_C = \alpha_B I_E + I_{CBO}$. As I_{CBO} is small relative to $\alpha_B I_E$, the effect on I_C is negligible. By using the relationships $I_E = I_C + I_B$ and $\alpha_E = \alpha_B / 1 - \alpha_B$ it can be proved that

$$I_C = \alpha_E I_B + \frac{I_{CBO}}{1 - \alpha_B}$$

The first term here is the value of I_C which we have so far taken as the output of the common-emitter configuration when the input current is I_B. The second term represents the leakage current when $I_B = 0$, that is, when the base is disconnected. This is denoted by I_{CEO}. Hence

$$I_{CEO} = I_{CBO} \times \frac{1}{1 - \alpha_B}$$

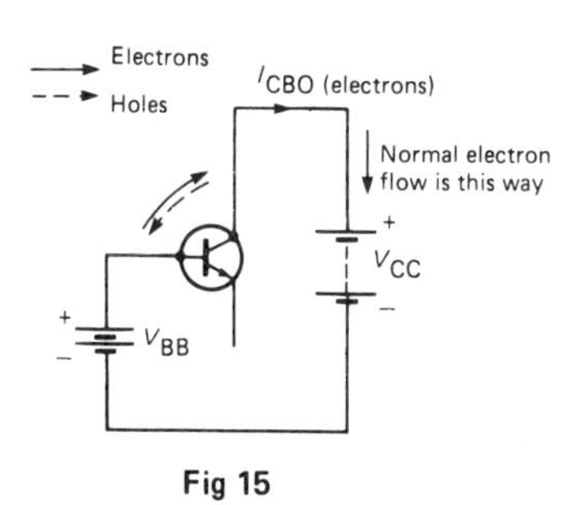

Fig 15

Since $1/1 - \alpha_B$ is very large, typically 100, I_{CEO} is one hundred times as large as I_{CBO}.

Hence the effect of leakage current on I_C is no longer of negligible proportions. A common-emitter circuit is not as inherently stable as a common-base circuit.

Problem 5 Discuss the different power dissipations taking place in a common-emitter amplifier stage both in the absence of an input signal and with one.

All power dissipated in the amplifier circuit is provided by the supply source. In the absence of a signal, the source supplies power to the transistor and the load resistor.

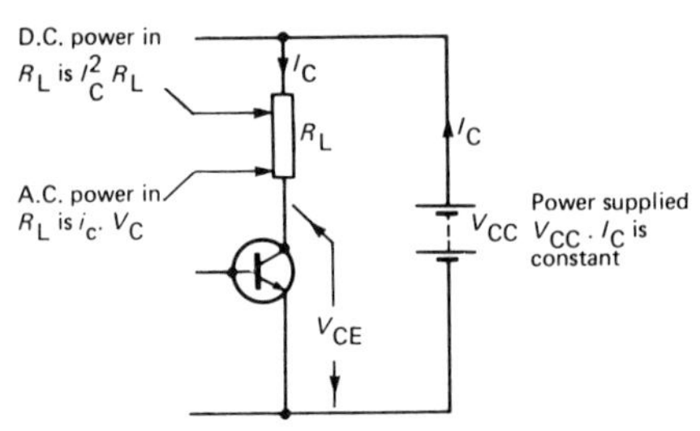

Fig 16

From *Fig 16*, these powers are given by:

(a) the product of I_C and V_{CE} which is dissipated as heat at the collector of the transistor; this is known as the **collector dissipation** (P_C) and it has a definite limit for any particular transistor.

(b) the product of $I_C{}^2$ and R_L, which is dissipated as heat in the collector load (P_L d.c.)

The sum of these powers must equal the supplied power given by $V_{CC} . I_C$. This is wasted power and is being dissipated whether a signal is present or not.

When a signal is applied at the base, an alternating current and an alternating voltage appear at the collector load; the product of the r.m.s. values of this current and voltage represent the *signal power* in the load (P_L a.c.) Since the $I_C{}^2 R_L$ dissipation in the load is constant and the power supplied $V_{CC} . I_C$ is also constant (since I_C, R_L and V_{CC} are all constant), the a.c. power which is developed in the load must be obtained at the expense of the collector dissipation. Hence, as the signal power *increases*, the collector dissipation *falls* and the transistor runs cooler.

It can be proved that the signal power output cannot exceed 25% of the power supplied, so at best the amplifier can be only 25% efficient.

Problem 6 How might a transistor be used to act as a switching element?

We have seen earlier how a diode behaves as an automatic switch, OPEN to forward voltages and CLOSED to reverse voltages. A transistor can also be used as a switch because it can be changed from a high resistance in its cut-off state (switch open) to a low resistance in its saturated state (switch closed). Intermediate conditions are of no importance, unlike the use of a transistor as an amplifier.

Base current is amplified by the transistor and the collector current increases as the base current input increases, finally reaching a limiting value determined by the transistor itself and the associated components. The base-emitter diode of the transistor, when conducting, has a voltage drop across it of about 0.6 V and this is substantially constant irrespective of the current passing. By placing current-limiting resistors in both the base and collector leads, a practical transistor switch becomes as shown in *Fig 17*. When V_i is at zero volts, no base current flows and the transistor is non-conducting. The output V_o is then at the level of V_{cc}. If now V_i rises to +1 V, say, the base emitter voltage is 0.6 V and the remainder of the applied input (0.4 V) develops across the 470 Ω base resistor. The current flowing into the base is then 0.4/470 A or 0.85 mA. This switches the transistor on (or **saturates** it) and the collector voltage falls to a very low value, typically 0.1 V.

Both on and off conditions are best illustrated by a look at the output characteristic and the load line suited to the collector load used, see *Fig 18*. When the input is zero, the

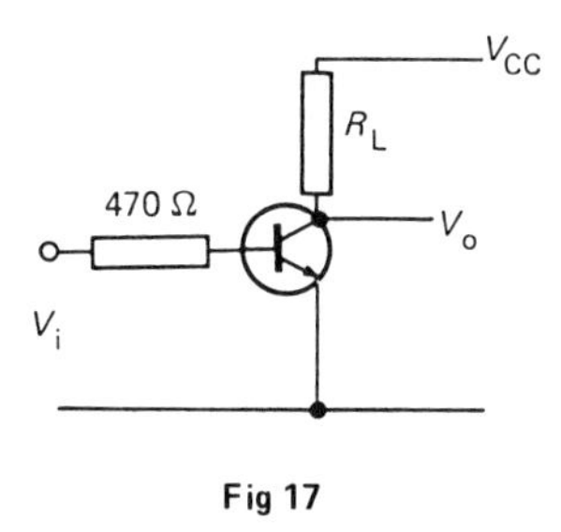

Fig 17

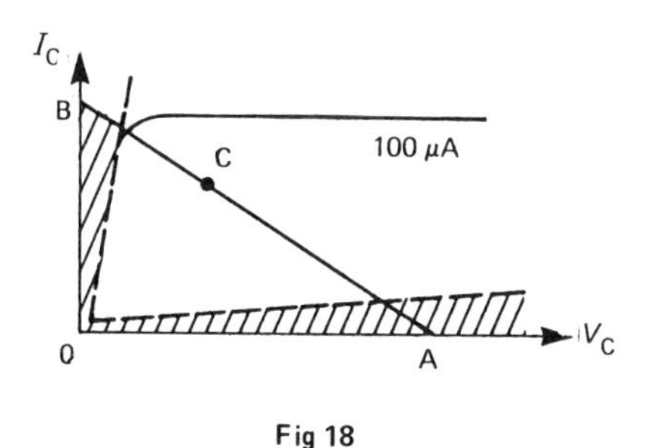

Fig 18

operating point is located at A; the shaded cut-off region is exaggerated for clarity. The switch whose 'contacts' are the collector and emitter terminals is then OPEN. When the input voltage is positive enough, the operating point moves to B. Any further increases in base current (in this example) above 100 μA produces no further increase in collector current; it remains at a value given closely by V_{cc}/R_L. This is the saturated or bottomed state. The switch contacts are then CLOSED. At any point on the line such as C the transistor is switched on but *not* saturated. All such intermediate positions on the line outside of the shaded areas do not produce an effective switch which has a low contact resistance when closed or a high contact resistance when open.

The applications of the transistor as a switch are many, particularly in logic where circuits operate strictly under ON or OFF conditions.

C. FURTHER PROBLEMS ON SMALL SIGNAL AMPLIFIERS

(a) SHORT ANSWER PROBLEMS (answers on page 133)

1 State whether the following statements are true or false:
   (a) The purpose of a transistor amplifier is to increase the frequency of an input signal.
   (b) The gain of an amplifier is the ratio of the output signal amplitude to the input signal amplitude.

(c) The output characteristics of a transistor relate the collector current to the base voltage.
(d) The equation of the load line is $V_{CE} = V_{CC} - I_C R_L$
(e) If the load resistor value is increased the load line gradient is reduced.
(f) In a common-emitter amplifier, the output voltage is shifted through 180° with reference to the input voltage.
(g) In a common-emitter amplifier, the input and output current are in phase.
(h) If the temperature of a transistor increases, V_{BE}, I_C and α_E all increase.
(j) A heat sink operates by artificially increasing the surface area of a transistor.
(k) The dynamic current gain of a transistor is always greater than the static current gain.

2 Complete the following statements:
(a) An increase in base current causes collector current to ....
(b) When base current increases, the voltage drop across the load resistor ....
(c) Under no-signal conditions the power supplied by the battery to an amplifier equals the power dissipated in the load plus the power dissipated in the ....
(d) The load line has a .... gradient.
(e) The gradient of the load line depends upon the value of ....
(f) The position of the load line depends upon ....
(g) The current gain of a common-emitter amplifier is always greater than ....
(h) The operating point is generally positioned at the .... of the load line.

3 An amplifier has $A_i = 50$, $A_V = 35$. What is the power gain?

4 What will be the gradient of a load line for a load resistor of value 5 kΩ? What units (if any) is the gradient measured in?

5 A transistor amplifier, supplied from a 9 V battery, requires a d.c. bias current of 100 μA. What value of bias resistor would be connected from base to the V_{CC} line (a) if V_{CE} is ignored (b) if V_{CE} is 0.6 V?

6 The transistor of *Problem 5* has $\alpha_E = 40$ and is used with a load resistor of 1.5 kΩ. What will be the mean collector voltage?

(b) MULTI–CHOICE PROBLEMS (answers on page 133)

1 Consider the amplifier shown in *Fig 19*. Select the correct answer to each of the following questions.

(i) If R_L went short circuit:
(a) the amplifier signal output would fall to zero;
(b) the collector current would fall to zero;
(c) the transistor would overload.

(ii) If R_2 went open circuit:
(a) the amplifier signal output would fall to zero;
(b) the operating point would be affected and the signal would distort;
(c) the input signal would not be applied to the base.

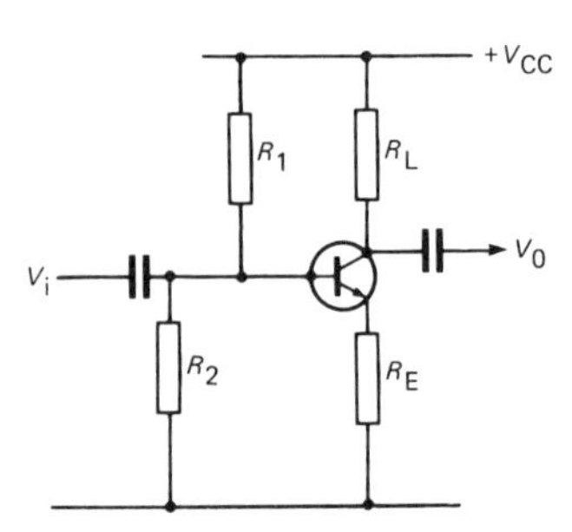

Fig 19

(iii) A voltmeter connected across R_E reads zero. Most probably
(a) the transistor base-emitter junction has short-circuited;
(b) R_L has gone open circuit;
(c) R_2 has gone short circuit.

(iv) A voltmeter connected across R_L reads zero. Most probably
(a) the V_{CC} supply battery is flat;
(b) the base collector junction of the transistor has gone open circuit;
(c) R_L has gone open circuit.

(v) If R_E went short circuit
(a) the load line would be unaffected;
(b) the load line would be affected.

2 Consider the output characteristics shown in *Fig 20* and select the correct answer to the following questions:

(i) the load line represents a load resistor of
(a) 1 kΩ; (b) 2 kΩ; (c) 3 kΩ.

(ii) the no-signal collector dissipation for the operating point marked X is
(a) 12 mW; (b) 15 mW; (c) 18 mW.

(iii) the greatest permissible peak input current would be about
(a) 30 μA; (b) 35 μA; (c) 60 μA.

(iv) the greatest possible peak output voltage would then be about
(a) 5.2 V; (b) 6.5 V; (c) 8.8 V.

(v) the power dissipated in the load resistor under no-signal conditions is:
(a) 16 mW; (b) 18 mW; (c) 20 mW.

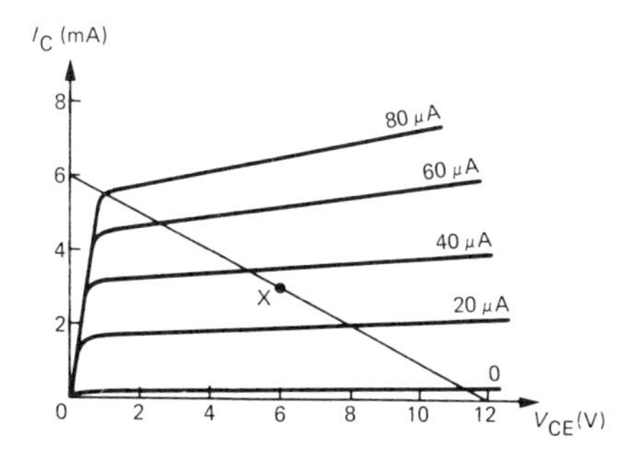

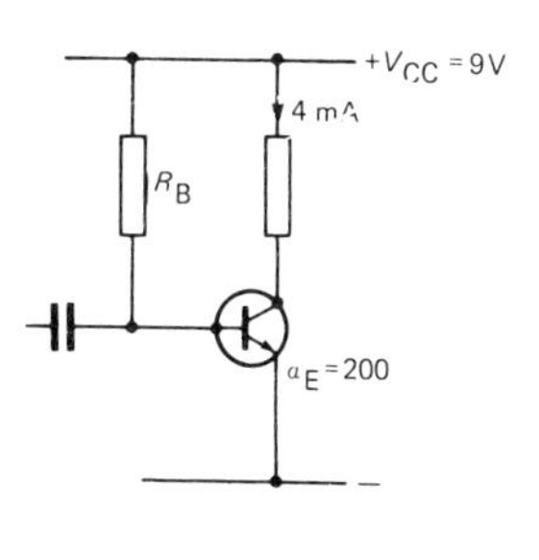

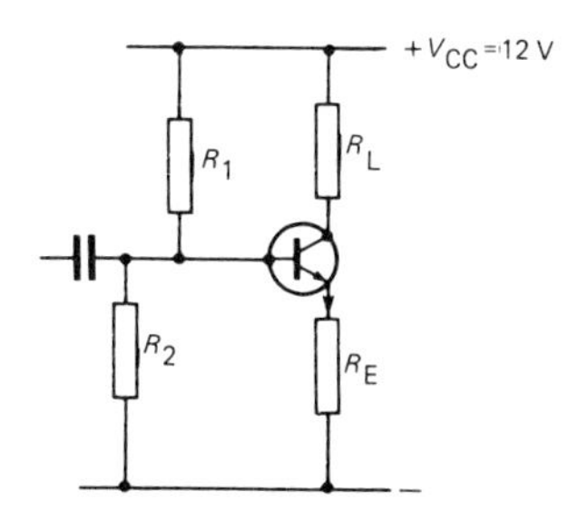

Fig 20 (above, left)

Fig 21 (above, right)

Fig 22 (left)

(c) CONVENTIONAL PROBLEMS

1 Draw a circuit diagram showing how a transistor can be used a common-emitter. Explain the purpose of all the components you show in your diagram.

2 A transistor with $\alpha_E = 200$ is used in the amplifier circuit of *Fig 21*. The base is biased so that the collector current is 4 mA. Taking $V_{BE} = 0.6$ V, calculate the value of resistor R_B.

[420 kΩ]

3 *Fig 22* shows a common-emitter amplifier with bias resistors R_1 and R_2 and emitter resistor R_E. Explain the purpose of these components. If the d.c. base bias current is 50 μA and the base-emitter voltage is 0.7 V, *assess* suitable values for R_1, R_2, R_E and R_L, given that a 1 V drop occurs across R_E.

[R_1 = 18.7 kΩ; R_2 = 3.4 kΩ, R_E = 1 kΩ; R_L = 5.5 kΩ]

4 Prove that voltage gain A_V can be expressed as $\alpha_E \cdot R_L/R_i$ and that power gain can be expressed as $\alpha_E \cdot V_O/V_i$.

5 Explain what is meant by thermal runaway. Make a diagram showing how a chain of events can lead to thermal runaway. Why is thermal runaway more likely in a germanium transistor than in a silicon transistor?

6 A transistor is connected as a common-emitter amplifier with R_L = 10 kΩ. The static current gain α_E is 100 and the input resistance R_i is 1 kΩ. What are the voltage and power gains of the amplifier?

[$A_V = 1000$; $A_p = 10^5$]

7 The output characteristics of a transistor in common-emitter configuration can be regarded as straight lines connecting the following points

	I_B = 20 μA		50 μA		80 μA	
V_{CE} (V)	1.0	8.0	1.0	8.0	1.0	8.0
I_C (mA)	1.2	1.4	3.4	4.2	6.1	8.1

Plot the characteristics and superimpose the load line for a 1 kΩ load. The supply voltage is 9 V and the d.c. base bias is 50 μA. Determine
(a) the quiescent collector current; (b) the collector power dissipation;
(c) the peak voltage output if the peak value of a sinusoidal base signal is 30 μA.

[(a) 4 mA; (b) 19.2 mW; (c) 2.5 V]

8 Plot the characteristic curves indicated in the following table:

	I_B = 10 μA		40 μA		70 μA	
V_{CE} (V)	1.0	7.0	1.0	7.0	1.0	7.0
I_C (mA)	0.6	0.7	2.5	2.9	4.6	5.35

Draw a load line for a 1.5 kΩ load through an operating point where I_B = 40 μA and V_{CE} = 4 V. Hence obtain (a) the collector current at the operating point; (b) the required supply voltage; (c) the current gain for a sinusoidal input of 30 μA peak.

[(a) 2.7 mA; (b) 8 V; (c) 63]

9 Using the characteristic of *Problem 8*, estimate for no-signal conditions (a) V_{CE}; (b) voltage across the load resistor; (c) I_C; (d) current through the load resistor; (e) the power dissipated in the transistor; (f) the power dissipated in the load; (g) the power taken from the supply.

[(a) 4 V; (b) 4 V; (c) 2.7 mA; (d) 2.7 mA; (e) 10.8 mW; (f) 11 mW; (g) 21.8 mW]

6 The field-effect transistor

A. MAIN POINTS CONCERNED WITH THE PRINCIPLES OF OPERATION OF THE FIELD-EFFECT TRANSISTOR

1 The field-effect transistor (FET) operates upon a completely different principle from bipolar transistors. In the bipolar transistor the junction is in series with the main current path from emitter to collector and the operation depends upon the injection of majority carriers from the emitter into the base. There is no such injection in FETs which depend only upon one effective p-n junction and only one type of charge carrier. For this reason FETs are known as **unipolar** devices. As an amplifier the FET has a very high input impedance, generates less noise than a bipolar transistor, has high power gain and a good high-frequency performance. In addition, although its voltage gain is lower than that obtainable from bipolar devices, it has a large input signal voltage handling capability. It is a voltage-operated device and the current drawn by the input is negligible. It is thus particularly useful where the input signal comes from a source which is unable to provide an appreciable current.

FETs are basically of two types: the junction gate FET (or JUGFET) and the insulated gate FET (or IGFET).

2 (i) The symbol for the junction gate FET is shown in *Fig 1(a)* and the form of construction in *Fig 1(b)*. The transistor is manufactured, as are bipolar transistors, by the planar method and consists essentially of a length of n-type (or p-type) semiconductor with ohmic (non-rectifying) contacts positioned at each end, together with two p-type (or n-type) regions known as **gates**. The length of semiconductor is known as the **channel** and the end connections as the **source** and the **drain** respectively. If the source is earthed and the drain terminal taken to a positive potential (V_{DS}), then assuming an n-type channel, electrons will flow along the channel from source to drain as

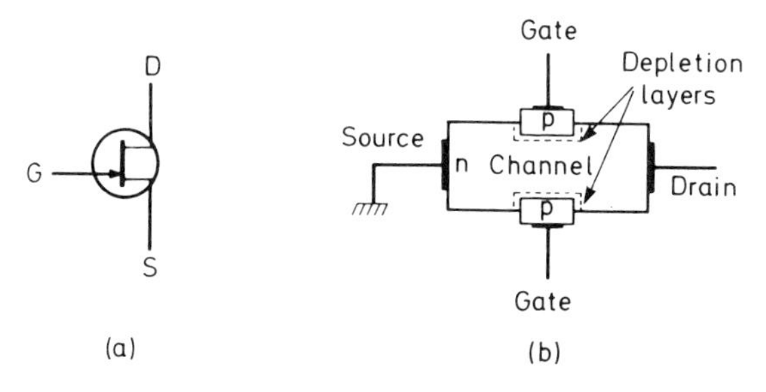

Fig 1

the charge carriers. As the channel has a finite resistivity there will be an approximately linear potential gradient established along the channel from source to drain.

(ii) Clearly the resistance of the source-drain path is a direct function of the effective dimensions of the channel. If the effective cross-sectional area of the channel can be varied in some way, the flow of current along it will come under external control. Such control can be effected by the gate electrodes. If the gates are short-circuited to the source, the positive potential V_{DS} being maintained between source and drain, the gates will form reverse-biased p-n junctions with the channel material, and depletion layers will be established as shown by the shaded areas in *Fig 2.* These layers will not be uniform but will be widest at the drain end. This is because the reverse bias is greater at that end than it is at the source end due to the potential gradient along the channel. Thus, current flow is restricted to the wedge-shaped path shown and the channel resistance has been increased.

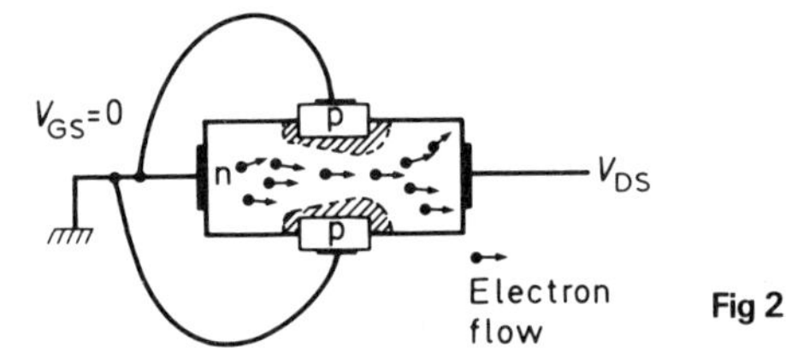

Fig 2

(iii) If the drain voltage is increased, the depletion layers will grow and eventually meet. The channel is then said to be **pinched-off.** The resistance of the channel is then very high and will remain high for further increases in V_{DS}. Notice particularly here that the pinch-off voltage is defined in terms of that value of V_{DS} which just causes the depletion layers to close across the channel.

3 (i) Characteristic curves can be drawn relating the drain-source voltage V_{DS} to the channel or drain current I_D. In *Fig 3* the line OA represents the behaviour of the channel acting simply as a semiconductor resistor; V_{DS} and I_D would be directly proportional to each other as stated by Ohm's law. The effect of the increasing resistance of the channel as V_{DS} increases causes the characteristic to depart from this linear relationship. At point B the curve bends over, becoming almost horizontal beyond this point, where pinch-off occurs and the value of **drain voltage** is the pinch-off voltage V_p. The drain current which flows when $V_{GS} = 0$ and $V_{DS} = V_P$ is denoted by I_{DSS}, representing the constant drain current with the input terminals short-circuited, i.e. gates connected to source.

(ii) If the gates are now negatively biased relative to the source, the depletion layers will clearly be 'thicker' for a given value of V_{DS} than they were when the bias was zero. Pinch-off and the onset of constancy in I_D will consequently occur at **lower** values of V_{DS}. A family of characteristics may be plotted in this way, V_{GS} being progreessively increased (negatively) relative to the source. Such curves are shown in *Fig 3,* each curve carrying the particular value of $-V_{GS}$ to which it relates. The superficial similarity of these curves (as regards shape) to the collector characteristics of bipolar transistors should be noted. The broken line in the diagram represents the locus of a point passing through the respective pinch-off locations on each of the curves. This line

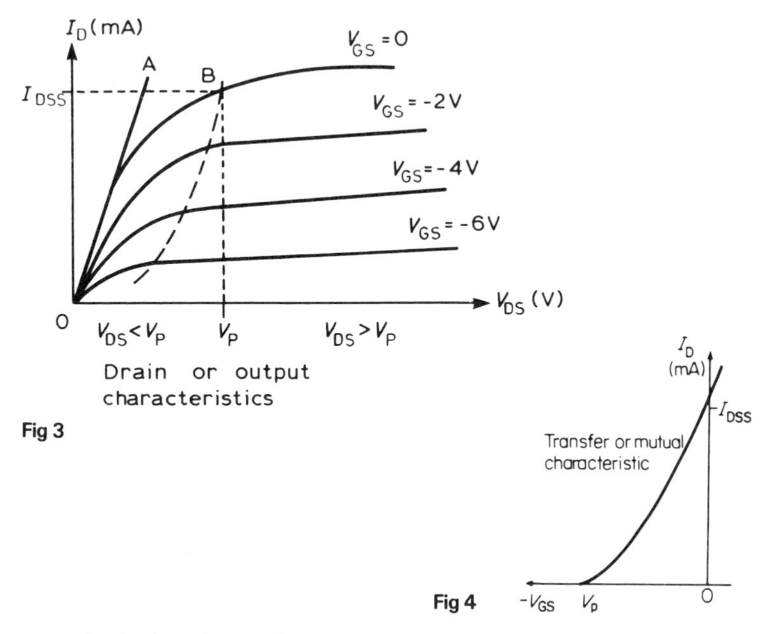

Fig 3

Fig 4

closely obeys the equation

$$|V_{DS}| = |V_P| - |V_{GS}|$$

To the left of the broken line the FET behaves as a variable resistor and this region is known as the **ohmic** region. To the right of the line the FET behaves as a constant-current generator having a high output resistance. The FET is normally operated in this **saturation** (or pinch-off) region where values of V_{DS} exceed V_P.

(iii) A second characteristic relating drain current I_D to V_{GS} can also be derived. This is the **transfer** or **mutual** characteristic and a typical curve (for a fixed value of V_{DS}) is shown in *Fig 4*. Notice that the particular value of I_D for which V_{GS} is zero is I_{DSS}. The pinch-off voltage appears on this characteristic in a different sense to what it appeared on the previous characteristics. Here V_P is defined in terms of that value of $-V_{GS}$ at which I_D is reduced to zero. This follows because V_P can be looked on as that voltage which, when applied between gate and source in the reverse direction, cuts off the drain current. Both interpretations of the pinch-off voltage, here and in sub-section 2(iii), can be shown to be identical.

4 (i) The insulated gate FET or the metal-oxide semiconductor FET or MOSFET, differs from the junction gate FET in that the gate is actually isolated from the channel by a very thin layer of oxide insulation, usually silicon dioxide (glass). The input resistance is then very much greater than that exhibited by the JUGFET, 10^6 MΩ or more relative to perhaps a few hundred megohms. MOSFETs are described under two general forms: the **depletion** type and the **enhancement** type.

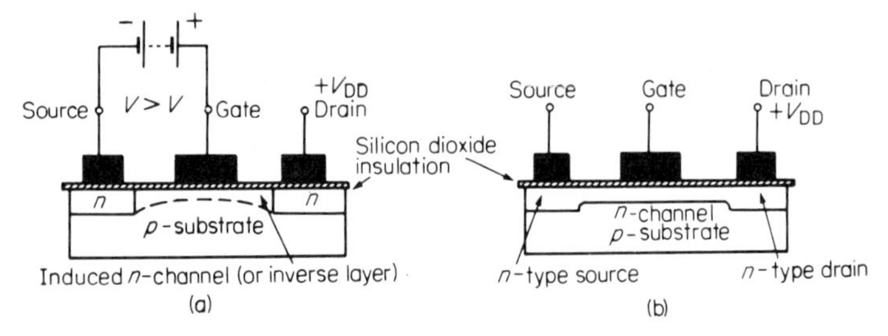

Fig 5

(ii) *Fig 5(a)* and *(b)* illustrates the constructional features of the enhancement and depletion type MOSFETs respectively. In both forms, the gate and channel form the two plates of a capacitor separated by the thin film of silicon dioxide. Because the gate is insulated in this way, V_{GS} can be either negative *or* positive with respect to the channel without forward conduction taking place through the gate-channel junction. Any potential applied to the gate establishes a charge on the gate and this induces an equal but oppositely signed charge in the surface of the substrate.

(iii) In *Fig 5(a),* when the gate potential is positive, a negative charge is induced in the p-type substrate at its interface with the silicon dioxide dielectric. This charge repels holes from the surface of the substrate and the minority carriers that remain (electrons) form an n-channel bridge which connects together the existing n-type source and drain electrodes. When the drain is connected to a positive supply, electrons flow from source to drain by way of the induced n-channel. Increasing V_{GS} **positively** widens or **enhances** the induced channel and the flow of drain current increases. Hence the name 'enhancement FET'.

When drain current flows along the channel, a voltage gradient is established and this tends to **cancel** the field set up across the dielectric by the positive gate charge. When the cancellation is sufficient almost to eliminate the induced n-channel layer, the channel pinches off and the drain current saturates at a value which, like the JUGFET, is practically independent of any further increases in drain voltage. The output and transfer characteristic curves for an n-channel enhancement FET are sketched in *Fig 6,* together with the circuit symbol. Notice from the transfer curve that no drain current

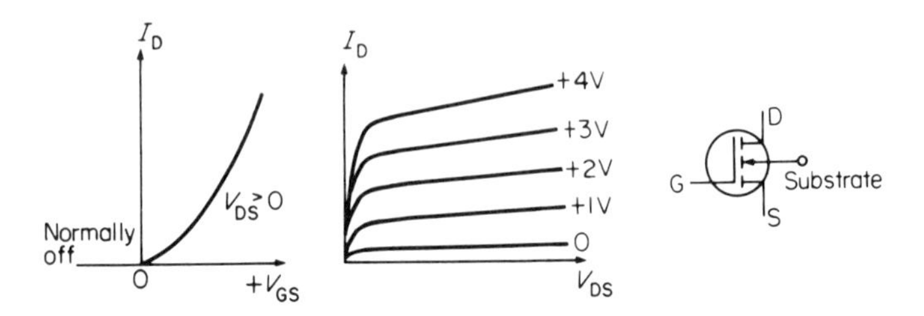

Fig 6

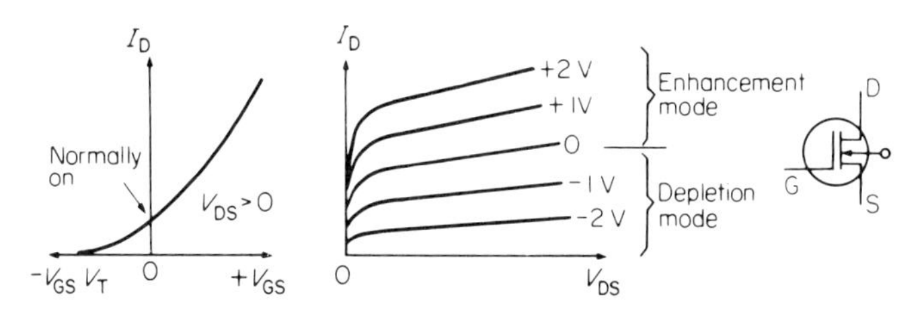

Fig 7

flows if the gate is made negative with respect to the source. The enhancement FET is normally an OFF device.

(iv) *Fig 5(b)* shows the construction of an n-channel depletion-mode MOSFET. Here the n-channel is introduced during manufacture by suitably doping the surface layer of the substrate between the source and drain electrodes. The device then resembles the JUGFET except for the oxide layer dielectric between gate and channel. As a result, current flows from source to drain with zero gate voltage whenever the drain is made positive. If the gate is made **negative** with respect to the channel, the n-channel width is reduced (or depleted) as electrons are repelled from its interface with the dielectric, and drain current decreases. The transistor is then operating in the depletion mode, just as the JUGFET does. When the gate is made **positive** with respect to the source, the channel width is enhanced and drain current increases. Hence this type of MOSFET will operate in either the depletion or enhancement modes.

Fig 7 shows the output and transfer characteristics of this transistor together with the circuit symbol. Notice that the gate voltage for zero drain current is now negative and that the transfer curve crosses the I_D axis where $V_{GS} = 0$ and $I_D = I_{DSS}$. Because I_D is not zero when V_{GS} is zero, the depletion FET is a normally ON device.

B. WORKED PROBLEMS ON FIELD-EFFECT TRANSISTORS

Problem 1 Define the static parameters of a FET necessary to express the performance of the device as an amplifier.

In the bipolar transistor our basic parameters were current gain, and input and output resistance. In the FET, drain **current** I_D is controlled by gate source **voltage** V_{GS}. Thus an expression for the circuit gain is of the form I_D/V_{GS}, which has the units of conductance, i.e. siemens. The term used is mutual- or trans-conductance, usually given the symbol g_m or g_{fs}. Then

$$g_m = \frac{\text{change in drain current } I_D}{\text{change in } V_{GS}} = \frac{\delta I_D}{\delta V_{GS}}$$

which is recognised as representing the **gradient** of the transfer characteristic, (see *Fig 4*). If I_D is in milliamperes and V_{GS} in volts, g_m is in millisiemens (mS). Often, however, g_m is expressed as mA/V.

Thus if a FET has a transconductance of 4 mS, a change in V_{GS} of 1 V causes a change in I_D of 4 mA. It is assumed that the drain voltage remains constant. A typical range of transconductance for FETs is 1 to 7 mS.

The other parameter of interest is the **drain slope resistance** denoted by r_{ds} and expressed as

$$r_{ds} = \frac{\text{change in } V_{DS}}{\text{change in } I_D} = \frac{\delta V_{DS}}{\delta I_D} \text{ for a constant } V_{GS}$$

This parameter, relating the dependence of drain current I_D upon the drain-source voltage V_{DS} represents the reciprocal of the gradient of the output characteristic (*Fig 3*) in the saturation region. Since the curves are very flat, r_{ds} and hence the output resistance of the transistor is very high.

Strictly no meaning can be attached to the current gain of a FET as it could for a bipolar device, since the input current can be considered negligible.

Problem 2 Define the amplification factor of a FET.

The drain current I_D of a FET can be controlled in two ways, either by varying V_{DS} (as shown on the output characteristics) or by varying V_{GS} (as shown on the transfer characteristic). For a given voltage variation, V_{GS} exerts a much greater influence on I_D than does V_{DS}. Suppose a small increase in V_{DS} causes an increase in I_D and that I_D is then **restored** to its original value by a small negative change in V_{GS}. The ratio of these two changes in V_{DS} and V_{GS} which have produced the **same** change in I_D is the amplification factor of the FET. This is symbolised by the Greek letter μ. Hence

$$\mu = \frac{\text{the small change in } V_{DS}}{\text{the small change in } V_{GS}} \text{ for the same change in } I_D$$

$$\mu = \frac{\delta V_{DS}}{\delta V_{GS}} \text{ for constant } I_D$$

μ is simply a ratio. It is related to the other two parameters g_m and r_{ds} for

$$\frac{\delta I_D}{\delta V_{GS}} \times \frac{\delta V_{DS}}{\delta I_D} = \frac{\delta V_{DS}}{\delta V_{GS}}$$

Hence $\mu = g_m \cdot r_{ds}$

Problem 3 Sketch a circuit of a FET voltage amplifier and explain its operation.

As with a bipolar transistor, a voltage amplifier using a FET is required to convert the output current into an output voltage. A load resistor must therefore be connected in the output circuit. *Fig 8(a)* shows the basic circuit arrangement for a **common-source** FET voltage amplifier, using a junction gate device. The load resistor R_L is connected into the drain circuit and the d.c. supply, denoted as V_{DD}, is applied as shown. The source terminal is returned to the earth line and a small negative bias is applied to the gate by the battery wired in series with the gate resistor R_G. A signal **voltage** applied at the input terminals causes the gate potential to vary about this mean d.c. bias, and the consequent variations in the width of the gate-source junction depletion layer controls the drain current and hence the output signal voltage developed across R_L.

It is not convenient to use a separate battery for the gate bias and a practical form of the circuit is shown in *Fig 8(b).* Here a resistor R_S is included in the source lead and the gate is connected to earth directly through R_G. Although this last resistor may have a value of many megohms to avoid appreciable shunting of the inherently high input resistance of the FET, the gate is at earth potential (from the d.c. point of view) because the gate current flowing through R_G is negligible. At the same time, R_G presents a very high impedance to the a.c. signal input. Since the drain current flows through R_S, a voltage drop equal to $I_D R_S$ appears across this resistor and the source is maintained a volt or so positive with respect to earth (and hence to the gate) by this potential. In this way the gate is held negative with respect to the source. This is known as **automatic biasing.** The

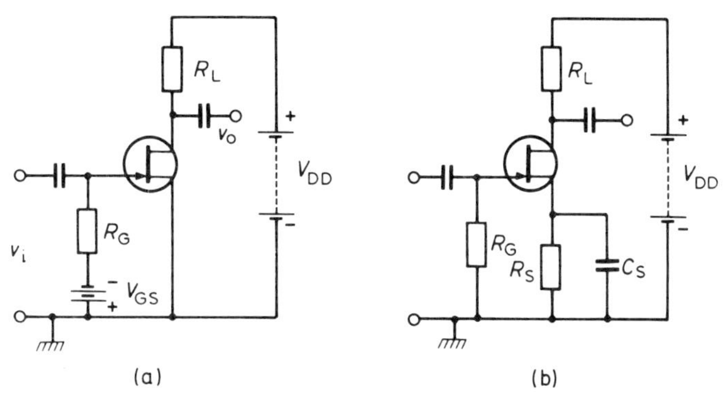

Fig 8

bias is actually dependent upon the source current in so far that if the source current rises, the gate bias is increased and the source current tends to be reduced, and conversely. In this way the amplifier can tolerate wide variations in its bias requirements which a simple battery supply, as shown earlier, will not provide. The capacitor C_S shunting R_S acts as a short-circuit to any **signal** variations developed on the source and so prevents signal negative, feedback which would otherwise seriously reduce the voltage gain.

Problem 4 Derive an expression for the voltage gain of a common-source FET amplifier as discussed in the previous solution.

Referring back to the basic circuit of *Fig 8(a),* let the signal input voltage be v_i and the signal output voltage developed across R_L be v_o. Then, from our definition of mutual conductance g_m,

$i_d = g_m \cdot v_i$

where i_d is the signal drain current. The output voltage is then

$v_o = -i_d \cdot R_L = -g_m \cdot v_i \cdot R_L$

The negative sign indicates that the drain potential falls when i_d rises, and vice-versa, i.e. a 180° voltage phase shift occurs in the amplifier. From these equations, the voltage gain

$$A_v = \frac{v_o}{v_i} = -g_m \cdot R_L$$

This formula is actually an approximation because the output resistance of the FET, r_{ds}, has been ignored. If r_{ds} is very large relative to R_L (as it usually is in practice) the formula is reasonably accurate. A more precise formula including the effect of r_{ds} can be derived and this gives

$$A_v = -\frac{r_{ds} g_m R_L}{r_{ds} + R_L} = -\frac{\mu \cdot R_L}{r_{ds} + R_L}$$

since $\mu = r_{ds} g_m$.

Problem 5 A voltage gain of 20 is required from a common-source FET amplifier where g_m = 2.5 mS and r_{ds} = 100 kΩ. What should be the value of the drain load resistor?;

$$A_v = 20 = \frac{100 \times 10^3 \times 2.5 \times 10^{-3} \times R_L}{(100 \times 10^3) + R_L}$$

$$20(R_L + 10^5) = 250\,R_L$$

$$230\,R_L = 20 \times 10^5$$

$$R_L = 8696\ \Omega$$

Notice that the negative sign has not appeared since the gain itself is strictly expressed as –20. Using the approximate formula, R_L works out as 8000 Ω. An 8.2 kΩ resistor would be suitable in practice.

Problem 6 Why, when pinch-off occurs in a FET and the depletion layers just meet across the width of the channel, does the drain current become substantially constant instead of falling to zero?

Drain current does not cease at pinch-off because a voltage equal to V_P still exists between the pinch-off point and the source, and the consequent electric field existing along the channel causes the carriers (electrons for an n-channel FET) to drift from source to drain. As V_{DS} is increased beyond V_P the depletion layers thicken as shown in *Fig 9(a)* and the additional drain voltage is effectively absorbed by the increased field in the wider pinched-off region. The electric field between the original pinch-off point and the source remains substantially

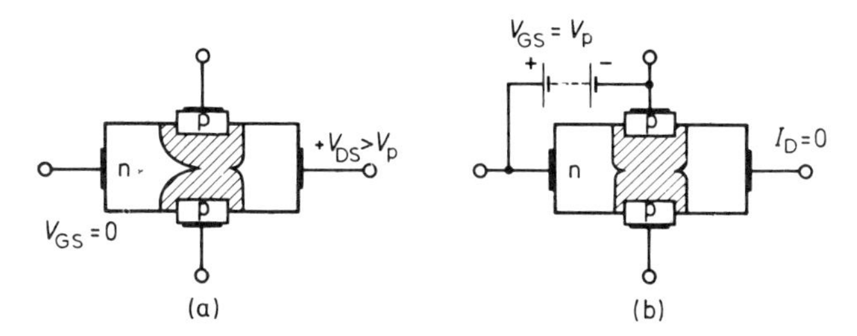

Fig 9

unaffected, hence the channel current remains constant. Electrons which arrive at the pinch-off point find themselves faced by a positive potential and are swept through the depletion layer region in exactly the same way as they are swept from base to collector in a bipolar n-p-n transistor. Drain current cut-off will occur if the *gate-resource* potential V_{GS} is made sufficiently negative to eliminate the electric field between the source and the original pinch-off point. This situation is illustrated in *Fig 9(b)*.

Problem 7 The following table shows the relationship between the drain current I_D and the drain source voltage V_{DS} of a FET for different values of V_{GS}.

V_{DS} (V)	I_D (mA) $V_{GS} = 0$	$V_{GS} = -1$ V	$V_{GS} = -2$ V
0	0	0	0
0.5	2.0	1.0	0.5
1.0	3.3	1.75	0.95
2.0	3.75	2.50	1.0
5.0	3.90	2.60	1.02
8.0	4.05	2.70	1.05

Plot the output characteristics and from them estimate (a) the mutual conductance g_m at $V_{DS} = 5$ V, (b) the output resistance r_{ds} for $V_{GS} = -1$ V. Obtain a figure for the amplification factor of the FET.

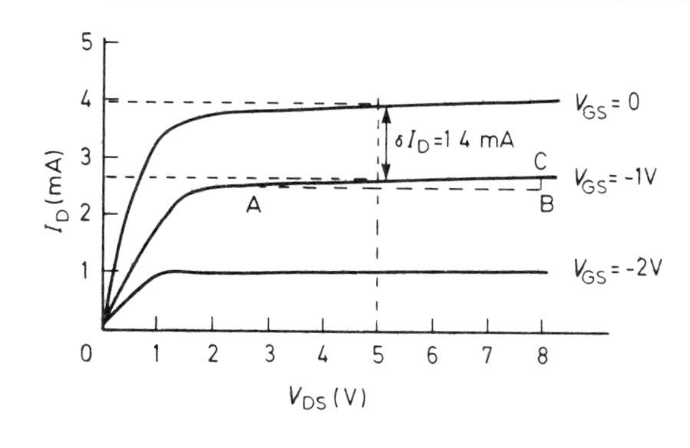

Fig 10

The curves are shown in *Fig 10.*

We have defined g_m as $\delta I_D/\delta V_{GS}$ with V_{DS} constant, in this case at 5 V. Erecting a perpendicular from the point where $V_{DS} = 5$ V, it is seen that a 1 V change in V_{GS} from −1 V to 0 V produces a change of I_D of 1.4 mA. Therefore

$$g_m = \frac{1.4}{1} \times 10^{-3} = \mathbf{1.4\ mS} \text{ (or 1.4 mA/V)}$$

From the triangle ABC drawn on the $V_{GS} = -1$ V characteristic, it is seen that a change in V_{DS} from 2.5 V to 8 V produces a change in I_D of about 0.2 mA. Therefore

$$r_{ds} = \frac{V_{DS}}{I_D} = \frac{8-2.5}{0.2 \times 10^{-3}}$$

$$= \mathbf{27\,500\ \Omega}$$

The amplification factor δ is given by the product $g_m r_{ds}$, hence

$$\mu = 1.4 \times 10^{-3} \times 27\,500 = \mathbf{38.5}$$

Problem 8 Great care is required when handling insulated gate FETs. Explain why this is so.

The low-leakage gate insulation of MOSFETs means that these transistors are very vulnerable to the build up of static charges on the gate and consequently high gate voltages. These voltages can break down the silicon dioxide layer and render the FET useless. Only a small charge, introduced by an unearthed soldering iron or even the tip of a finger, will lead to a very large voltage build up on the small capacitance concerned. For example, suppose the gate-channel capacitance to be only 1 pF, then a charge of only 1 μC can theoretically lead to a voltage of 1 megavolt! For this reason, MOSFETs are supplied on pieces of conducting foam plastic or metal foil which short-circuits all the pins together. When being fitted into circuit the MOSFET (particularly if it is part of a complicated integrated circuit) should not have its pins handled and the soldering iron used should be securely earthed. For integrated circuits, a holder should be used in preference to the direct soldering of the device to a printed board. A protection network of back-to-back Zener diodes is often incorporated across the input of MOSFET devices or can be externally added. This technique does, however, degrade the otherwise high input impedance of the MOSFET.

C. FURTHER PROBLEMS ON THE FIELD-EFFECT TRANSISTOR

(a) SHORT ANSWER PROBLEMS

1 Why is a FET referred to as a unipolar device?
2 Sketch the constructional form and describe the principle of operation of a junction-gate FET.
3. Compare the properties of a field-effect transistor with those of a bipolar transistor.
4 Why has an insulated-gate FET to be carefully handled?

5 What do the terms V_p and I_{DSS} represent?

6 Define the FET parameters g_m, r_{ds} and μ.

7 Which type of FET will operate in either the depletion or the enhancement mode?

8 Sketch a circuit diagram of an automatically-biased junction gate FET used as a common-source amplifier and explain its operation.

9 Sketch the circuit symbol for (a) a JUGFET, (b) a depletion type MOSFET, (c) an enhancement type MOSFET.

10 Complete the following statements:
(a) A JUGFET can operate only in the . . . mode, (b) I_{DSS} is the drain current that flows when v_{GS} = . . . (c) In an n-channel JUGFET, majority carriers are . . . and they flow from . . . to . . . (d) The . . . FET is a normally 'ON' device, (e) The . . . FET is a normally 'OFF' device, (f) In the enhancement FET, carriers flow from source to drain by way of the . . . channel, (g) In a p-channel JUGFET the gate should be biased . . . with respect to the source and the drain should be . . . with respect to the source.

(b) MULTI–CHOICE PROBLEMS (answers on page 133)

1 The field-effect transistor which can be used either in the depletion or the enhancement mode is (a) the junction gate FET, (b) the depletion MOSFET, (c) the enhancement MOSFET.

2 In an insulated-gate FET the gate is isolated from the channel by (a) an induced n-channel, (b) an induced p-channel, (c) an oxide layer, (d) the substrate.

3 In an enhancement type FET the drain current that flows when the gate-source voltage is zero is (a) very large, (b) very small, (c) zero

4 The characteristic curves shown in *Fig 11* are those of (a) an n-channel JUGFET, (b) a p-channel JUGFET, (c) an n-channel depletion MOSFET, (d) a p-channel enhancement MOSFET.

5 When the drain-source voltage of a junction FET is zero, the depletion layers at the gate-channel junction are (a) not present, (b) present but of negligible thickness, (c) present and of appreciable thickness, (d) just meeting across the channel.

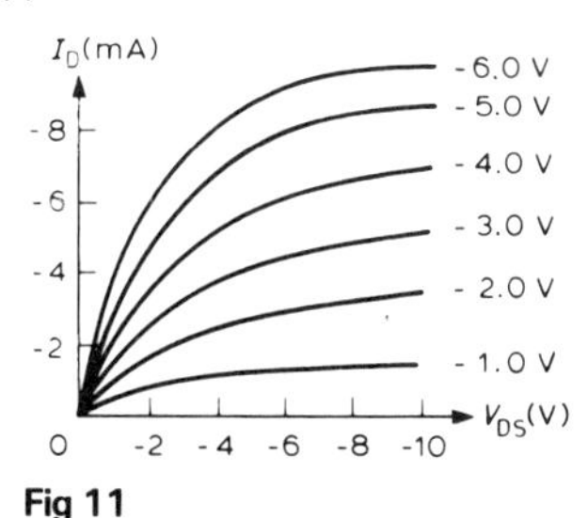

Fig 11

6 When pinch-off is reached in a junction gate FET, further increases in drain-source voltage (a) narrow the pinch-off region, (b) widen the pinch-off region, (c) have no effect on the pinch-off region, (d) cause drain current to fall to zero.

7 The output resistance r_{ds} of a FET can be obtained from (a) the gradient of the transfer characteristic, (b) the gradient of the drain characteristic, (c) a measurement of the resistance of the channel, (d) the value of the drain load resistor.

8 If the gate of an n-channel JUGFET is taken positive with respect to the source, (a) the input resistance becomes very low, (b) the input resistance becomes very high, (c) the input resistance is unaffected.

(c) CONVENTIONAL PROBLEMS

1 In the common-source amplifier, the FET parameters are $g_m = 2.0$ mS, $r_{ds} = 50$ kΩ. If the load resistor is 22 kΩ, what is the voltage gain? [–30.6]

2 What value of load resistor would be required for the amplifier of the previous question if the voltage gain was to be –20? [12.5 kΩ]

3 The following values were taken from the linear portions of the static characteristics of a certain FET:

V_{DS}(V)	15	15	10
I_D (mA)	13.5	10.5	12.7
V_{GS} (V)	-0.5	-1.0	-0.5

Obtain values for the parameters g_m, r_{ds} and μ for this FET. [6 mS, 6250 Ω, 37.5]

4 Describe the principle of operation and sketch the circuit symbol for both the depletion and enhancement types of insulated gate FETs. Draw typical output characteristics for these FETs.

5 Explain why thermal runaway is not likely to be the problem with FETs that it is with bipolar transistors.

6 A FET has a transconductance of 4.4 mS. If the gate-source voltage is changed by 1 V, what will be the change in drain current? What assumption have you made in obtaining your answer? [4.4 mA]

7 When the drain voltage of a FET is reduced from 15 V to 5 V the drain current falls from 2.0 mA to 1.5 mA. Assuming a constant V_{GS}, estimate the output resistance of the FET. [20 kΩ]

8 The output characteristics of a FET are given in the following table. Plot these characteristics and determine the value of r_{ds} from the characteristic for $V_{gs} = -2$ V. Use the curves to estimate the mutual conductance of the FET for $V_{DS} = 5$ V.

V_{DS} (V)	I_D (mA)			
	V_{GS}0	-1.0	–2.0	–3.0
2.0	5.6	4.15	3.0	1.90
6.0	7.0	5.25	3.62	1.91
9.0	8.1	6.0	4.1	1.92

[6670 Ω, 1.7 mS]

9 It can be shown that the equation for the drain current of a FET is given approximately by the form

$$I_D = I_{DSS}\left\{1 - \left[\frac{V_{GS}}{V_p}\right]^2\right\} \text{ mA}$$

for a given value of V_{DS}. Given that $I_{DSS} = 7.5$ mA, calculate I_D for each of these values of V_{GS}: 0, –0.5, –1, –1.5, –2 and –2.5 V. Plot the mutual characteristic for this transistor and estimate the value of g_m when $V_{GS} = -1.5$ V, given that $V_p = -2.5$ V. [2 mS]

10 The output of a source of e.m.f. 2 mV and internal resistance 500 Ω is to be amplified to produce a voltage of 120 mV. Calculate the value of load resistor required (a) for a bipolar transistor having $h_{ie} = 1.5$ kΩ, $h_{fe} = 60$, with h_{re} and h_{oe} negligible; (b) for a junction gate FET having $g_m = 5$ mS, $r_{ds} = 40$ kΩ. (C & G 1976)

[(a) 2kΩ, (b) 17.1 kΩ]

11 In the amplifier shown earlier in *Fig 8(b)*, $V_p = -2$ V and $I_{DSS} = 2.0$ mA. It is desired to bias the circuit at $I_D = 1.1$ mA, V_{DD} being 15 V. Calculate (i) V_{GS}; (ii) g_m; (iii) R_S; (iv) the required value of R_L to provide a voltage gain of 10, (v) the quiescent V_{DS}.

[(i) 0.52 V; (ii) 1.48 mS; (iii) 470 Ω; (iv) 6.75 kΩ; (v) 7.1 V]

12 A FET amplifier of the form shown in *Fig 8(b)* is to have a voltage gain of 14.5. Capacitor C_s has a reactance equal to one-tenth the value of R_s at a frequency of 50 Hz. If $V_p = -2$ V, $I_{DSS} = 2.0$ mA, $I_D = 1.0$ mA, calculate V_{GS}, g_m, R_s, R_L and C_s. Assume that $r_d \gg R_L$.

[-0.58 V; 1.42 mS; 580 Ω; 8.5 kΩ; 55 μF]

7 Stabilised power supplies

A. MAIN POINTS CONCERNED WITH STABILISING SYSTEMS

1 Direct current power supplies for electronic equipment are, apart from battery operated devices, obtained from rectified and smoothed a.c. mains supplies. The basic rectification systems have already been covered in Chapter 2 earlier, where the half-wave, full-wave and bridge circuits were discussed, together with smoothing.

Although these basic circuits are adequate for the supply of d.c. power to many electronic systems and the bridge circuit is very commonly used, they are unsuitable for more demanding conditions such as are imposed by the needs of d.c. amplifiers, stable oscillators and clocks, logic systems and computers, to name only a few. The output voltage from the basic circuits is dependent upon the stability of the input a.c. supply and the current actually being drawn by the load. Such supplies are unstabilised. A stabilised supply, on the other hand, is designed to provide a d.c. output free of ripple and which remains constant at a predetermined voltage level regardless of mains voltage or load current variations.

2 In the earlier chapter we discussed the zener diode as a simple stabilising element, and a brief recapitulation here is not out of place. The diode is wired in parallel with the load as shown in *Fig 1* and is fed current by way of a series of resistor R_s. At a particular value of terminal voltage, the zener, which is under reverse bias conditions, breaks down and thereafter the voltage across it, V_Z, remains substantially constant irrespective of changes in the current flowing through it. If the **input voltage** V_i should increase, the zener will pass a greater current so that the increased voltage drop across R_s will not change. Again the output voltage will remain relatively constant. Zener diodes are available with breakdown voltages ranging from about 2 V up to 200 V, with power ratings from 400 mW up to 20 W and more.

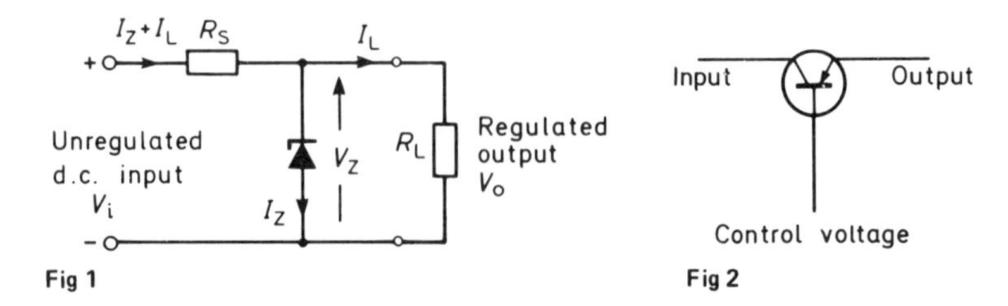

Fig 1

Fig 2

3 The zener diode is a **shunt** stabiliser. A **series** stabiliser provides a better form of control for many applications. The output from the rectifier is applied to a control element which introduces series resistance into the positive output line.

Such a series control can be a transistor capable of handling the required output current, connected as shown in *Fig 2*. A control voltage, whose magnitude depends upon any variation in the output level, is applied to the base of the transistor. The consequent variation in the effective resistance of the transistor then acts in such a direction that the output deviation is corrected.

4 The control transistor may be connected in parallel with the load to form a shunt stabiliser system (*Fig 4*). When the output voltage tends to rise above its design value, the resistance of the shunt transistor is reduced, allowing it to pass a larger current. The increased voltage drop across R_s then reduces the output voltage, and conversely. The transistor here is taking the place of the shunt zener stabiliser with the advantage that it can handle much larger currents than can a zener. Another advantage over series control is that the transistor does not need to be able to carry the full load current as it does in the series case. Further, an accidental short-circuit across the load terminals cannot damage the transistor. Shunt control is used where a fairly high and constant load current is called for. Series stabilisers are preferred for variable load current demands.

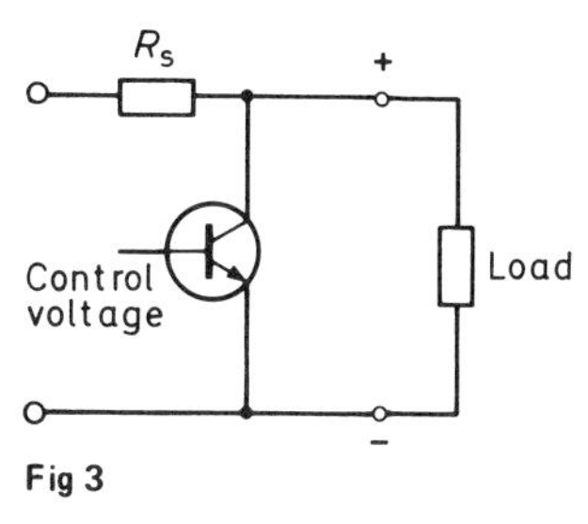

Fig 3

B WORKED PROBLEMS ON STABILISED POWER SUPPLIES

Problem 1 Explain how the operation of a zener diode differs from that of an ordinary diode. What is meant by zener slope resistance?

A zener diode is manufactured with a much narrower junction than an ordinary diode and has a relatively high impurity concentration. In the forward direction the zener characteristic is similar to that of an ordinary diode, but in the reverse direction breakdown occurs at much lower reverse voltage, starting as low as about 2 V; see *Fig 4*. When breakdown occurs, the electric field strength across the junction is sufficient to pull electrons out of their covalent bonds. This gives rise to an effect known as **field emission.** In an ordinary diode, breakdown occurs at much higher reverse voltages and results from accelerated minority carriers colliding with ions in the depletion layer. This releases more electrons from their covalent bonds and leads to so-called **avalanche** breakdown. Up to about 7 V, zener breakdown is attributable mainly to field emission. The breakdown point is known as the avalanche or zener point.

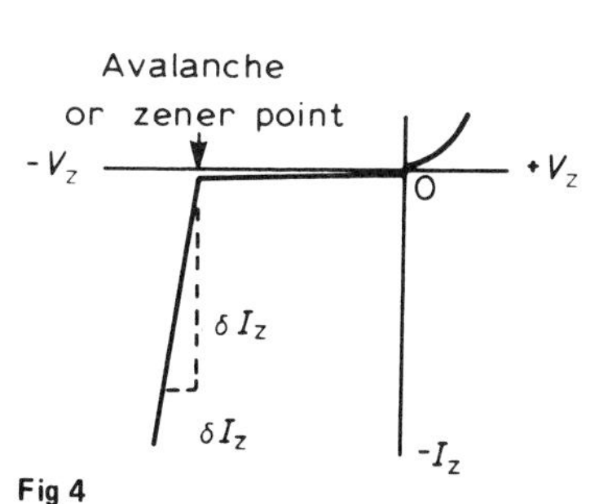

Fig 4

After breakdown the zener behaves as a linear resistor, the voltage across it increasing only slightly with further increases in current through it. A series resistor is used with a zener diode to limit the diode current to a safe value and prevents destruction of the device. Zener slope resistance is defined as

$$R_Z = \frac{\delta V_Z}{\delta I_Z} \Omega$$

Problem 2 A zener diode shunt stabiliser circuit is shown in *Fig 5*. Explain the calculations necessary in setting up such a circuit and describe briefly how the circuit stabilises against supply voltage and load current variation.;

Suppose the output terminals are open-circuited, that is, the load is disconnected. The zener will then take the maximum current and dissipate the maximum power. Hence

$$I_{z\,max} = \frac{\text{zener power rating}}{\text{zener voltage}}$$

The stabilised voltage V_o will be that existing across the zener. This will represent the difference between V_i and the voltage dropped across R_s when I_{max} is flowing, i.e.

$$V_o = V_i - I_{max} \cdot R_s$$

$$\therefore \quad R_s = \frac{V_i - V_o}{I_{max}}$$

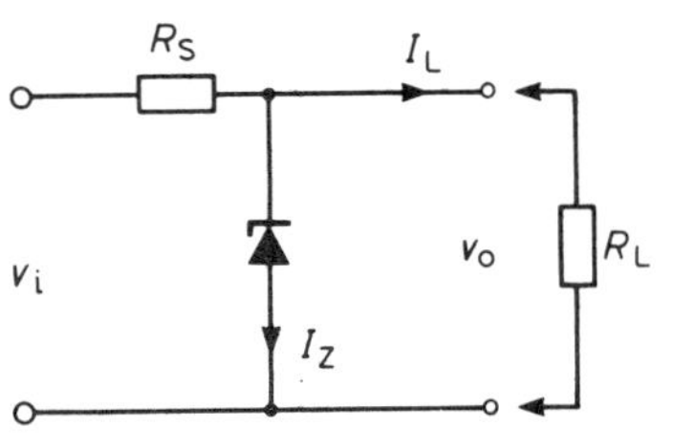

Fig 5

When a load R_L is connected, the load current I_L is taken up from the zener so that V_o will remain unchanged, because the total current through R_s remains unchanged and the voltage drop across it is still $V_o - V_i$. If the load varies, the zener gives up or accepts the current difference to maintain this condition. There is a **minimum** zener current for which stabilisation remains effective and I_z must not be allowed to fall below this. This is a function of the voltage across the zener and hence this condition represents the minimum value of the supply voltage V_i permissible. The ratio

$$S = \frac{\text{the small change in output voltage}}{\text{the small change in input voltage}} = \frac{\delta V_o}{\delta V_i}$$

with R_L constant is known as the **stability ratio.**

Problem 3 A 20 V stabilised output is required for a variable load from a nominal 45 V source. A 20 V, 3 W zener is available whose voltage remains constant down to a current of 1 mA. Calculate (a) the greatest variation in the supply voltage over which stabilisation will be effective if $R_L = 2$ kΩ, (b) the least value of load resistance permissible when the supply voltage is 45 V.

The circuit is sketched in *Fig 6*. To stabilise at 20 V from the 45 V source requires 25 V to be dropped across R_s. The zener is rated at 3 W, hence

$$I_{z\,max} = \frac{3}{20}\ \text{A} = 150\ \text{mA}$$

$$R_s = \frac{25}{150 \times 10^{-3}} = 167\ \Omega$$

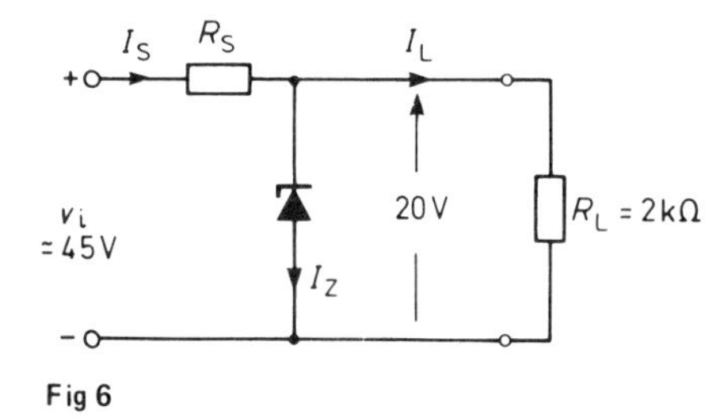

Fig 6

This is the absolute minimum value required for R_s. In practice a rather higher value would be selected to allow for the possibility of a rise in the input voltage.
(a) For the **minimum** value of supply voltage, the zener must still pass 1 mA.

Hence for $R_L = 2\ \text{k}\Omega$

$$I_L = \frac{20}{2000}\ \text{A} = 10\ \text{mA}$$

$$I_s = I_z + I_L = 11\ \text{mA}$$

$$\therefore \quad V_{i\,min} = (11 \times 10^{-3} \times 167) + 20 = \mathbf{21 \cdot 84\ V}$$

For the **maximum** value of supply voltage the zener current must not exceed $I_{z\,max} = 150$ mA.

$$\therefore \quad I_s = I_z + I_L = 160\ \text{mA}$$

$$\therefore \quad V_{i\,max} = (160 \times 10^{-3} \times 167) + 20 = \mathbf{46.7\ V}$$

(b) When $V_i = 45$ V the least value of R_L occurs when $I_z = 1$ mA.

$$I_s = \frac{25}{167}\ \text{A} = 150\ \text{mA}$$

$$\therefore \quad I_L = 150 - 1 = 149\ \text{mA}$$

$$\therefore \quad R_{L\,min} = \frac{20}{149 \times 10^{-3}} = \mathbf{134\Omega}$$

Problem 4 Describe the action of the circuit shown in *Fig 7*.

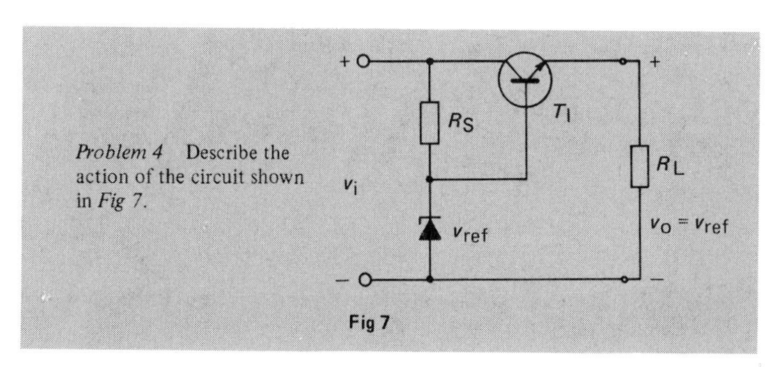

Fig 7

The stabilisation afforded by the simple shunt zener circuit would be improved if the magnitude of the current flowing in the diode could be reduced. This is done in the circuit illustrated by providing a current amplifier in conjunction with the zener which now acts only as a fixed voltage reference, V_{ref}. The zener is a shunt regulator supplied with current through a series resistor as previously described, but feeding the base of a transistor current amplifier as the actual control element. Since the transistor is connected as an emitter-follower, the voltage at its emitter (the load voltage) is practically equal to the base voltage. But the base is held at a constant voltage by the zener diode, hence the output voltage is constant. The base voltage is now the effective zener load and this can be relatively small in comparison with the load current drawn by way of the series power transistor T_1.

Problem 5 Draw the circuit diagram of a voltage stabiliser in which the output can be varied over a relatively wide range.

A circuit is shown in *Fig 8*. This bears some resemblance to that of *Fig 10* but an additional transistor T_2 has been added. The zener diode now maintains the emitter potential of T_2 at a constant level and the base of this transistor is held at a fraction of the output voltage by the setting of the potential divider resistor R_1. Resistor R_2 is chosen so that the base of T_2 is never at a voltage **lower** than that set by the reference at its emitter.

Suppose an output voltage change occurs for any reason. This change is sensed at the slider of R_1 and hence at the base of T_2. As the emitter potential is fixed, the base voltage change will either increase or decrease the current through T_2 according to the direction in which the base voltage has moved. The change in the collector voltage of T_2 is now fed to the base of the series control transistor T_1 where it adjusts the load current in such a direction that the original output variation is minimised. T_2 is known as the **voltage comparator** element because it compares the output voltage against the reference.

The capacitor C is included to enable the circuit to deal with rapid voltage variations. For a switching transient, for example, a sudden variation may occur at the output. This is transmitted by way of C immediately to the base of T_2 and compensation follows at once. For slow output variations the effect of C is negligible. The output voltage is

$$V_o = \left[\frac{R_1 + R_2}{R_2}\right] V_{ref} = \left[\frac{R_1}{R_2} + 1\right] V_{ref}$$

so that V_o can be adjusted by variation of the ratio R_1/R_2. The output voltage can never be less than V_{ref} so if control down to zero is required a negative supply line has to be provided.

Problem 6 If the output terminals of a series controlled power supply are accidentally short-circuited, the resulting current flow will damage the series transistor. How might protection be applied in a practical circuit?

There is no inherent short-circuit protection for the series regulator as there is for the shunt regulator. Protection can be provided to the series regulator by a

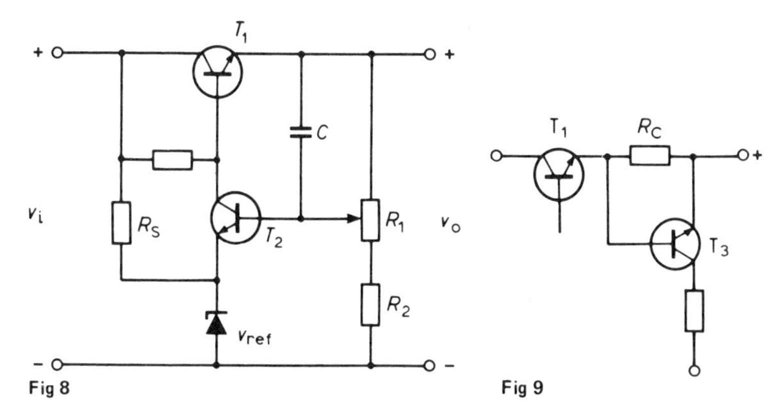

Fig 8

Fig 9

circuit of the form shown in *Fig 9*. A current-sensing resistor R_c is connected in series with the output line. Its value is chosen so that when a current in excess of the maximum passes through it, the voltage drop across it exceeds some 0.6 V and switches on transistor T_3 (which is the overload detector). The resulting collector current of T_3 is fed back and diverts base current from the comparator which in turns switches the series transistor back towards cut-off. The current is then held at a safe level until the overload condition is removed.

Problem 7 Integrated forms of voltage stabiliser are available. Describe how these are connected into a power supply unit.

A range of voltage stabilisers can be found in manufacturers' catalogues and obtained readily from electronic supply sources. These integrated circuits are

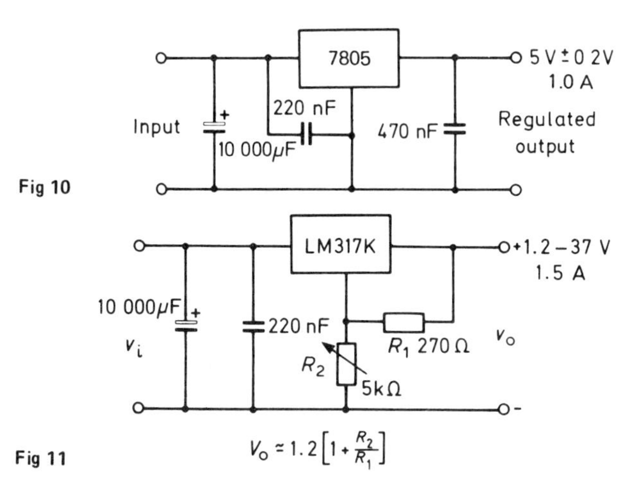

Fig 10

Fig 11

three- or four-terminal devices and are mounted usually in the familiar T0220 style packages. Both fixed voltage and variable output voltage types are available. All types have built-in overload protection. A typical fixed voltage circuit using the 7805 regulator is shown in *Fig 10* and provides a fixed 5 V output ±0.2 V at 1.0 A for an input voltage range of 7 to 35 V. 12 V and 15 V output types are also available as are 2A versions of this series.

For a variable output, types LM317K and 338K may be used, a typical circuit being shown in *Fig 11*. The 317K can provide an output of from 1.2 V to 37 V at 1.5 A for an input voltage range 4 to 40 V; the 338K has a similar output range at a current of 5 A. It is necessary to mount these devices on large heat sinks.

Problem 8 In the stabiliser shown in *Fig 12* the voltage gains of T_1 and T_2 are respectively 15 and 150. If the input voltage from the rectifier changes by 5 V, what will be the change in the output voltage?

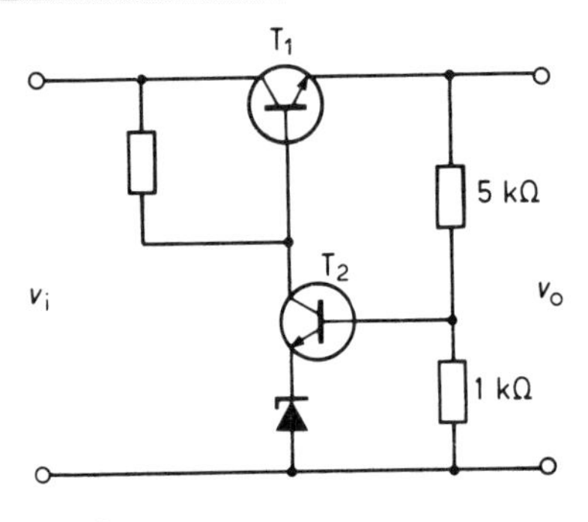

Fig 12

Let the output voltage change be δV_o. Then the change in voltage at the base of T_2 will be $\delta V_o/6$, because $(R_1+R_2)/R_2=(5+1)/1=6$.

The control voltage appearing at the collector of T_2 will be $A_{v2}\delta V_o/6$, where A_{v2} is the voltage gain of T_2. Hence the base–emitter voltage of T_1 will be

$$\frac{A_{v2}\delta V_o}{6} - \delta V_o = 25\,\delta V_o - \delta V_o$$

$$= 24\,\delta V_o$$

This will produce a voltage across T_1 equal to $15 \times 24\,\delta V_o = 360\,\delta V_o$.

But the voltage across T_1 is also equal to $5 - \delta V_o$. Hence

$$5 - \delta V_o = 360\,\delta V_o$$

$$\therefore \quad \delta V_o = \frac{5}{361} = \mathbf{0.014\,V} \text{ or } \mathbf{14\,mV}$$

C. FURTHER PROBLEMS ON STABILISED POWER SUPPLIES

(a) SHORT ANSWER PROBLEMS

1 What factors affect the output voltage of an unstabilised power unit?

2 Sketch a circuit diagram of a biphase rectifier and smoothing system.

3 Give the circuit diagram of a bridge rectifier and add wave diagrams to show how it operates. Deduce that there is no d.c. component of current flowing in the transformer winding.

4 Why is smoothing necessary after rectification has taken place?

5 The a.c. input to a bridge rectifier is 100 V r.m.s. What will be the mean value of the unsmoothed output? When smoothing is added, what will be the approximate value of the output voltage? [90 V, 140 V]

6 Describe in a few words the method of control provided by series and shunt stabilisers.

7 Differentiate between a stabilised and an unstabilised supply.

8 Explain the different effects of field emission and avalanche breakdown in a zener diode.

9 The voltage across a zener diode changes from 6.15 to 6.2 V when the current through it changes from 20 mA to 35 mA. What is the zener slope resistance? [3.33 Ω]

10 A zener diode has a reverse characteristic equation given by $V = 11 + 5I$, where V is in volts and I is in amperes, for values of I greater than 10 mA. What is the slope resistance of this zener? [5 Ω]

11 A 25 V stabilised voltage is required from a 35 V unstabilised supply. A 25 V zener is available with a power rating of 2 W. Find the required value of series resistor. [125 Ω]

12 Define stabilisation ratio. What would be the stabilisation ratio of a perfect regulator system? [zero]

13 In the circuit of *Fig 8* why cannot the output voltage be less than the reference levels?

(b) MULTI–CHOICE PROBLEMS (answers on page 133)

1 Adding a reservoir capacitor to a rectifier output (a) increases the mean voltage, (b) decreases the mean voltage, (c) leaves the mean voltage unaffected, (d) increases the ripple voltage.

2 The ripple frequency in a bridge or biphase circuit is (a) equal to the supply frequency, (b) equal to one-half the supply frequency, (c) equal to twice the supply frequency, (d) dependent upon the value of reservoir capacitor.

3 The purpose of a resistor in series with a zener shunt stabiliser is to (a) smooth the supply, (b) drop the input voltage to the desired level, (c) prevent the power rating of the zener being exceeded, (d) prevent damage if the output terminals are short-circuited.

4 The stabilisation efficiency of a zener regulator is improved if the (a) magnitude of the zener current is reduced, (b) magnitude of the zener current is increased, (c) zener is mounted on a heat sink, (d) series resistor is omitted.

5 A series stabiliser circuit is preferred to shunt if the (a) load is stable, (b) load is liable to wide variation, (c) output voltage is very low, (d) input voltage is very low.

6 In comparison with a series regulator, the control transistor in a shunt regulator has to (a) carry the full load current but has a lower voltage across it, (b) carry the full load current and have a higher voltage across it, (c) withstand a higher voltage but does not carry the full load current, (d) carry neither the full load current nor withstand the full output voltage.

7 The power dissipation in a shunt zener regulator is greatest when the (a) load is disconnected, (b) normal load is connected, (c) output is short-circuited, (d) the load is connected but the input is at its highest level.

8 When the input voltage to a shunt zener stabiliser circuit increases from 30 V to 32 V, the output voltage changes from 22 V to 22.01 V. The stabilisation ratio of the circuit is (a) 0.01, (b) 0,1, (c) 0.05, (d) 0.005.

(c) CONVENTIONAL PROBLEMS

1 A 20 V stabilised supply is required from a 40 V unstabilised d.c. source. A 20 V zener is to be used for this purpose having a power rating of 1.5 W. Find the required value of series resistor. [267 Ω]

2 A zener diode is to provide a 16 V stabilised output from a 20 V unstabilised supply. The load resistor $R_L = 2$ kΩ and the zener current $I_z = 8$ mA. What series resistor is required and what power is dissipated in it? [46 Ω, 350 mW]

3 In the circuit of *Fig 13* what is the maximum power dissipation in the zener diode? What is the greatest load current that can be drawn if the minimum zener current is 3 mA? [62.5 mW, 10.3 mA]

4 The slope resistance of the zener in *Problem 3* is 20 Ω. What will be the change in the no-load output voltage if the input voltage falls to one-half its present level? [180 mV]

5 Explain briefly how the operation of a zener diode differs from that of a conventional diode. Draw the circuit diagram of a simple zener stabilising circuit and calculate suitable component values to provide a 15 V d.c. stabilised supply to a variable load from a 40 V input. A 15 V, 4 W zener is used whose voltage remains constant down to a current of 0.5 mA.
[$R_s = 93.8$ Ω, smallest load resistance = 53.6 Ω]

6 The following data apply to a zener diode:

Nominal voltage at 5 mA current = 9 V
Maximum slope resistance at 5 mA = 10 Ω
The characteristic is linear above 0.5 mA.

Sketch a circuit diagram showing how this diode may be employed to supply a load of 15 mA at a constant voltage of 9 V from a d.c. source of nominal 24 V.
Calculate the load voltage variation when the supply voltage varies by 2 V.
[30 mV (C.&G.)]

7 A zener diode has a reverse characteristic equation $V = 9.1 + 5.01I$ (V in volts, I in amperes) for values of I greater than 0.01 A. It is used as a simple stabiliser for a load which can vary between 0 and 150 mA from a d.c. supply of nominal voltage 25V which may vary by ±5 V. Estimate the maximum value of the series resistor which may be used if the zener current is not to fall below 0.01 A for all input and load conditions. For this value of series resistor determine (a) the minimum power rating of the zener; (b) the maximum variation in output voltage. [67.8 Ω, (a) 3 W, (b) 1.39 V (C.&G.)]

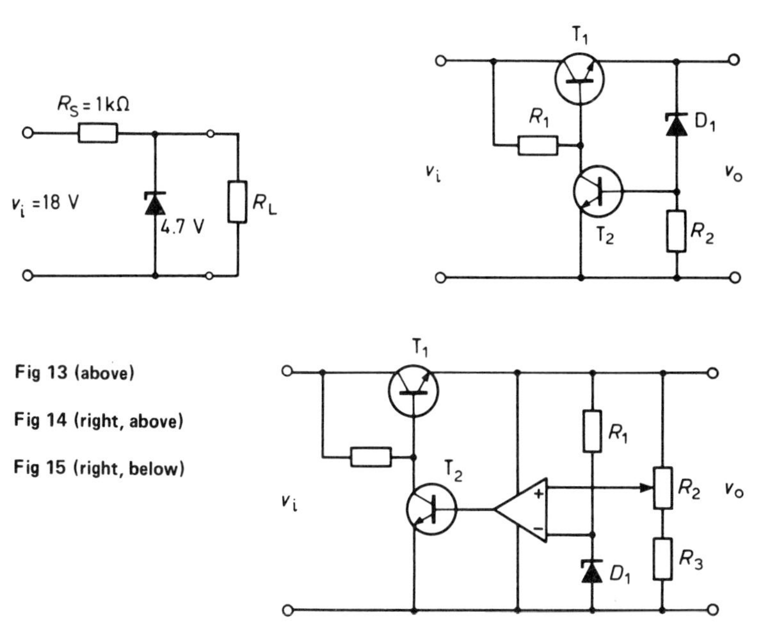

Fig 13 (above)

Fig 14 (right, above)

Fig 15 (right, below)

8 The voltage stability of a series stabiliser is better if the reference voltage is derived from the output voltage rather than from the input voltage. Explain why this is so.

9 A stabilised power supply is shown in *Fig 14*. Explain this function of each component used in this circuit. How does the circuit perform its stabilising action when (a) the input voltage is constant and load current changes, (b) the load current is constant but the input voltage changes.

10 *Fig 15* shows a regulator circuit using an operational amplifier as a comparator element. Explain how this circuit works and mention any advantage it might have over the circuit in *Fig 12*, for example.

8 Logic symbolism

A. MAIN POINTS CONCERNED WITH LOGIC SYMBOLISM

1 (i) In the simplest electrical circuit of *Fig 1* there are two possible states or conditions in which the circuit may be set; either switch S is closed and the lamp across termi[nals] A and B is ON, or switch S is open and the lamp is OFF. This is an elementary **two-state** system.

With such a system it is possible to transmit information from one place to another by using a prearranged code where the letters of the alphabet, for example, are represented by ordered arrangements of the ON and OFF states. A simple ON or OFF code conveys little information but a complex arrangement of LONG and SHORT signals with critical OFF periods form the basis of a comprehensive communications system. One such system is Morse Code, an everyday example of a two state language.

(ii) Why are two-state systems of importance? Because so many electrical and magneti[c] devices have essentially two stable states, ON and OFF. Whether the two states are referred to as ON and OFF is of no consequence; they might equally well be referr[ed] to as HIGH and LOW, PLUS and MINUS, FALSE and TRUE, depending upon the circumstances. In computing systems, the number symbols 0 and 1 represent the two possible states of a circuit or device. These are the symbols we shall normally use. The information can then be conveyed in binary form and arithmetical operations may be performed by using the binary scale of numbers which has only two digits 0 and 1.

2 Binary encoded information is best represented in an electrical form as a difference in voltage or current levels. This enables the levels to represent binary arithmetic. There must, however, be a decision as to which level in a particular system represents the symbol 0 or 1. In *Fig 2(a)*, the train of voltage signal pulses rise to a level 1 which

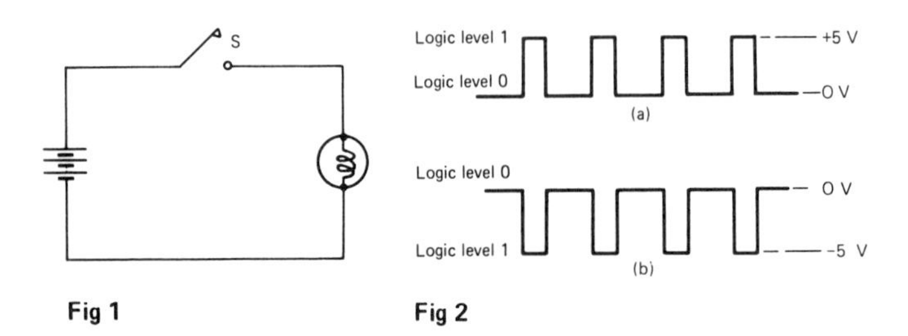

Fig 1

Fig 2

is positive with respect to level 0; in *Fig 2(b)* the pulses rise to a level 0 which is positive with respect to level 1. The following convention is used to differentiate between these two possibilities:

(a) **Positive logic** labels the more positive voltage (or current) level as the logic state 1 and the other voltage level as the logic state 0.

(b) **Negative logic** labels the more negative voltage level as the logic state 1 and the other voltage level as the logic state 0.

Make a careful note that neither level has necessarily to be at earth potential; it is the *relative* levels which determine the positive or negative logic conditions.

3 (i) Simple switching circuits provide a convenient starting point in the study of circuit logic because circuit devices such as relays, diodes and transistors can be switched on or off by two-state voltage or current codes.

In *Fig 3*, three switches A, B and C are connected in series with a battery (the voltage level state) and a lamp (the output signal state). The lamp F will be ON

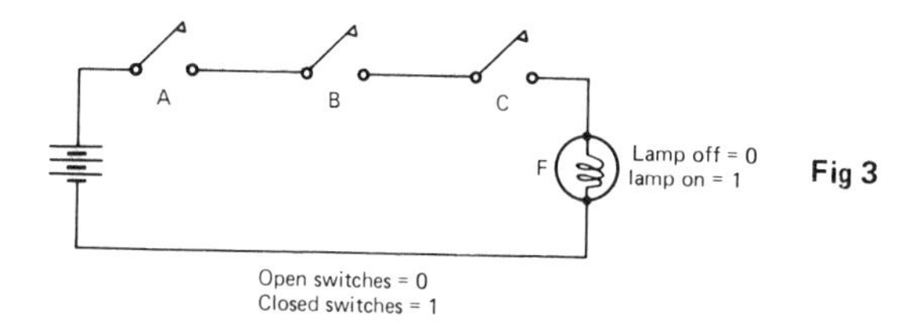

Fig 3

only if all three switches A, B and C are ON. If either A, B or C if OFF, or any combination of them are OFF, the lamp will be OFF. If an ON condition is represented by the symbol 1 and an OFF condition is represented by the symbol 0, then the output is 1 only if switches A *and* B *and* C are set at 1. We accordingly call such a series circuit a logical **AND** circuit. Hence

A.B.C = F, where the Boolean symbol for AND is a dot.

We can gather the information deduced from this circuit in the form of a table. This is called a truth table and for the circuit of *Fig 3* it will be as shown in *Table 1*.

TABLE 1

A	*B*	*C*	*F*
0	0	0	0
0	0	1	0
0	1	0	0
0	1	1	0
1	0	0	0
1	0	1	0
1	1	0	0
1	1	1	1

TABLE 2

A	*B*	*C*	*F*
0	0	0	0
0	0	1	1
0	1	0	1
0	1	1	1
1	0	0	1
1	0	1	1
1	1	0	1
1	1	1	1

Notice that there are 8 rows in the table. There are three switches each with two possible states or positions, so there are $2^3 = 8$ ways of combining these two states or positions. Out of all eight possibilities, there is an output F = 1 only if states A, B and C are all equal to 1. This corresponds to the last row in the table. All other conditions for A, B and C give F = 0.

(ii) Let the switches be connected in parallel as shown in *Fig. 4*. This time the lamp will light if either A *or* B or C is ON (= 1). We accordingly call such a parallel circuit a logical **OR** circuit. The truth table for the logical OR function is as shown in *Table 2*.

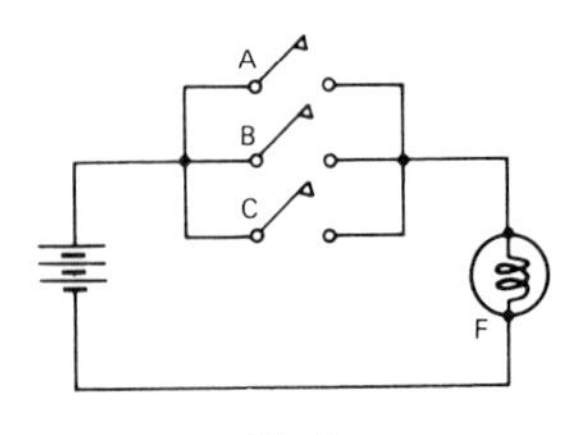

Fig 4

Again there are 8 rows in the table, and only if A or B or C is present is there an output F. The Boolean symbol for the OR function is + (sometimes v is used), so that A + B + C = F.

Although circuits using three series or parallel connected switches have been used in the above examples, quite obviously any number could be used to illustrate the basic AND and OR logical functions.

Electrical circuits which simulate the logical AND and OR functions are called **logic gates**.

4 In logic, if one position of a two-position switch is A, then the other position is not-A, symbolized as an A with a negation bar over it, $\bar{A}$. In a circuit, negation or NOT is represented by a system in which the output signal is the inverse of the input signal whatever the logic state of the input signal.

The truth table for the function is shown in *Table 3*. Only two possible combinations are shown since the NOT gate has one input and one output only.

TABLE 3

A	*F*
0	1
1	0

The Boolean representation of this operation is written $F = \bar{A}$.

5 We can use the logical AND, OR and NOT definitions to establish certain logical relations. A logical equation is not simply the equivalent of an algebraic equation in the ordinary sense and results which may at first glance be taken as obvious (or not obvious) are not necessarily so. By considering series and parallel connected switches we can establish some basic rules of logical algebra in both symbolic and circuit form. These basic rules are shown in *Table 4* on page 84.

6 Suppose there are two boxes, one containing the switching circuit of *Fig 5(a)* and the other the switching circuit shown in *Fig 5(b)*. The logical equation for circuit (a) is simply A = F. For circuit (b) we have a combination of series and parallel switches for which the logical equation is A + (A.B) = F. As before, the F simply signifies that an output signal is obtained when the switches A and B are operated in the manner indicated by the equations, in this second case being when A OR (A AND B) are operated.

Take a note that the two switches marked A are both operated together. Suppose now we write A + (A.B) = A.

Clearly this statement is true: if switch A in circuit (a) is operated the circuit is

TABLE 4

Logic	Meaning	Circuit
$0.0 = 0$	Open in series with open is open	
$0.1 = 0$	Open in series with closed is open	
$1.1 = 1$	Closed in series with closed is closed	
$A.\bar{A} = 0$	Switch in series with its negation is open	
$0 + 0 = 0$	Open in parallel with open is open	
$0 + 1 = 1$	Open in parallel with closed is closed	
$1 + 1 = 1$	Closed in parallel with closed is closed	
$A + \bar{A} = 1$	Switch in parallel with its negation is closed	

completed and an output is obtained. If switches A in circuit (b) are operated, the circuit is completed also. The presence of switch B is irrelevant. So too is the switch A in series with B. Only the upper switch A is strictly necessary, hence the three-switch circuit at (b) does only the same job as the single switch circuit at (a). Operationally, the two circuits are identical and their logical representations are equivalent.

The equivalence of two logical equations is a matter of great importance in the design of computers since the ability to reduce a complicated circuit to a simpler

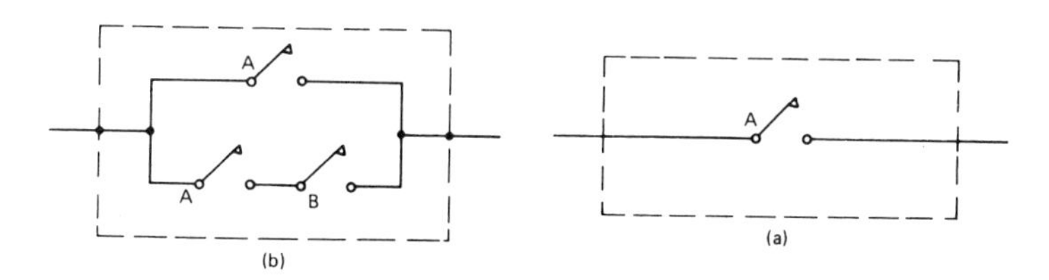

Fig 5

one doing exactly the same job enables the designer to use the minimum number of circuit elements or gates. It is not necessary to draw and compare two logical circuits as we did above to prove equivalence, in fact, such a procedure might be very difficult. There are several other methods of such proof, the simplest being a comparison of truth tables.

A truth table is constructed for each of the logical expressions we are testing for equivalence (or otherwise). If the two expressions have the same truth values for their respective output columns, then they are equivalent. If at any point of the truth values differ, then the expressions are not equivalent.

B. WORKED PROBLEMS ON LOGICAL SYMBOLISM

Problem 1 Complete the truth tables shown in *Table 5(a)* and *(b)*

TABLE 5

(a) AND gate

A	*B*	*F*
0	0	
0	1	
1	0	
1	1	

(b) OR gate

A	*B*	*F*
0	0	
0	1	
1	0	
1	1	

The truth tables are clearly for two-switch AND and OR gates. For the AND gate, there will be an output F only if both A and B are operated, that is, if A = 1 and B = 1. For the cases where A = 0, B = 0 and A = 0, B = 1 and A = 1, B = 0, the output will be 0. The table is therefore completed as shown in *Table 6(a)*.

For the OR gate, there will be an output if either A or B (or both are operated. Hence F = 1 when A = 1 or B = 1 or A.B = 1. For the case where A = 0, B = 0, there will be no output. The table is therefore completed as shown in *Table 6(b)*.

TABLE 6(a)

A	*B*	*F*
0	0	0
0	1	0
1	0	0
1	1	1

TABLE 6(b)

A	*B*	*F*
0	0	0
0	1	1
1	0	1
1	1	1

Problem 2 Distinguish between an inclusive OR gate and an exclusive OR gate. Draw a circuit illustrating the action of an exclusive OR gate, and construct the truth table.

The circuit of *Fig 6* (like that of *Fig 4*) provides an output not only when the switches are operated separately, but when they are operated in pairs or all together. Such an OR circuit is known as an **inclusive** gate, because it includes all possible combinations of the switch positions that provide an output at F. If, however, an output is obtained *only* when A = 1, or B = 1 but not when A.B = 1, the gate is known as an **exclusive** OR. One alternative now excludes all the others, there is no possibility of both. Hence $F = A.\bar{B} + B.\bar{A}$

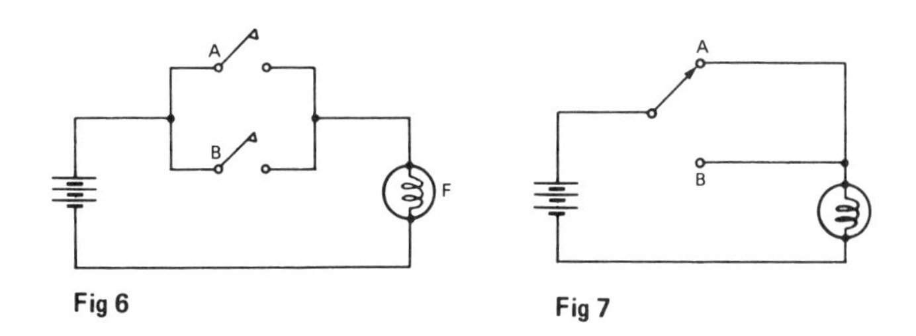

Fig 6

Fig 7

Fig 7 shows a circuit using a two-way or changeover switch that simulates an exclusive OR gate. Switch positions A or B will provide an output to the lamp, but a combination of A and B is not possible.

The truth table for an exclusive OR gate is shown in *Table 7*. This should be compared with the inclusive case shown in *Table 6(b)*

TABLE 7

A	*B*	*F*
0	0	0
0	1	1
1	0	1
1	1	0

Problem 3 Use truth tables and simple switching circuits to verify the following rules of Boolean algebra:
(a) $A + A = A$; (b) $A.A = A$; (c) $A + \bar{A} = 1$; (d) $A.\bar{A} = 0$.

Care must be taken in the interpretation of Boolean algebra because it often behaves in a somewhat different way to ordinary algebra. The symbols + and . stand for OR and AND and *not* for addition and multiplication and this in itself can often make logical expressions look very un-logical! The use of simple truth tables will always lead to the proper relationship, as this worked solution will illustrate.

(a) $A + A = A$. The truth table for this expression is

A	*A*	*A + A*
1	1	1
0	0	0

← A or A = A

Hence $A + A = A$. There is no interpretation to 2A.

(b) A.A. = A The truth table here is

A	*A*	*A.A*
1	1	1
0	0	0

← A and A = A

Hence $A.A = A$. There is no interpretation to A^2

(c) $A + \overline{A} = 1$. The truth table here is

A	$\overline{A}$	$A + \overline{A}$
1	0	1
0	1	1

← A or not-A = 1

(d) $A.\overline{A}. = 0$ The truth table here is

A	$\overline{A}$	$A.\overline{A}$
1	0	0
0	1	0

← A and not-A = 0

Figs 8(a) to (d) illustrates the switching circuits that will stimulate these four logical rules.

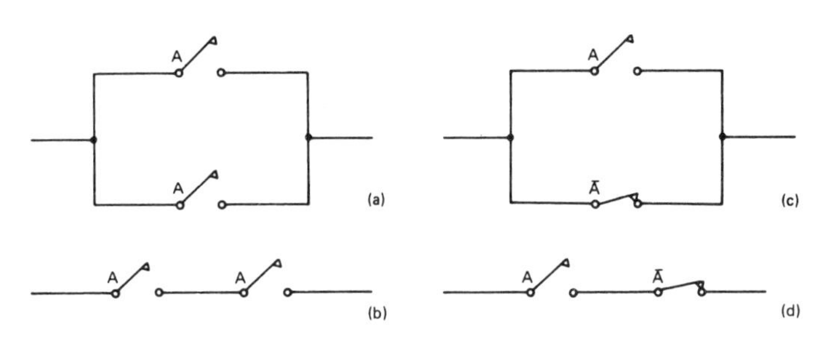

Fig 8

Problem 4 Prove, using a truth table, that $A + \overline{A}.B = A + B$ and illustrate the equivalence in terms of switching circuits.

There are only two component parts to the given equation, A and B. Consequently, the first two columns of the truth table should allow for all the possible switching positions of these in terms of 0 and 1: there will clearly be $2^2 = 4$ possibilities.

The term $\overline{A}$ can then be placed in a third column, $\overline{A}.B$ in a fourth, and so on, until all the terms involved have been accounted for. This procedure then leads to the following table:

A	B	$\overline{A}$	$\overline{A}.B$	$A + \overline{A}.B$	$A + B$
0	0	1	0	0	0
0	1	1	1	1	1
1	0	0	0	1	1
1	1	0	0	1	1

The third column ($\overline{A}$) is the negation of the first column (A). The fourth column is the logical AND function for $\overline{A}.B$ and has the value 1 only when $\overline{A}$ and B are simultaneously equal to 1 i.e. the second row condition. The fifth column is the logical OR function and has the value 1 when either the (A) column or the ($\overline{A}.B.$) column, or both, have the value 1. The last column has the OR function A + B.

Comparison of the fifth column with the sixth shows them to be identical, hence the statement $A + \overline{A}.B. = A.B$ is true.

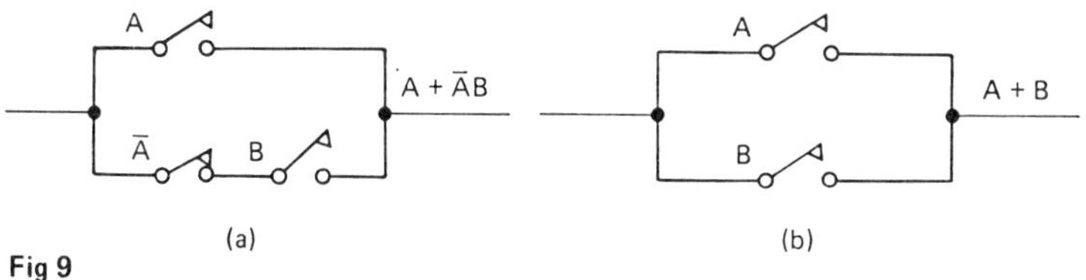

Fig 9

Fig 9(a) and (b) shows the switching circuit representations of A + A.B and A + B respectively. These should be identical in circuit function. In (a) the circuit is completed if A is closed (note that $\bar{A}$ then opens) or if A is left open (so that $\bar{A}$ remains closed) and B is closed i.e. A + $\bar{A}$.B is satisfied. So all that is necessary for the closing of the circuit is the closure of A or B. Circuit (b) representing A + B is then identical to circuit (a).

Problem 5 A signal A is stated to be expressed as 101011. Explain what this means? If the signal is applied to a NOT gate, what will the output signal be? If a signal B = 110101 is applied with signal A to a two-input AND gate what will the output signal be?

The signal represents the binary number 101011. This number is represented electrically as a train of pulses. Assuming positive logic, 1 will be represented by a high voltage level and 0 by a low (or zero) voltage level. If you look back at *Fig 2(a)* the pulse train there shown would represent the binary number . . . . . 001001001 . . . the time spent at the 0 level being each time twice as long as the time spent at the 1 level, hence representing two successive 0 levels to each 1 level.

When A = 101011 is applied to a NOT gate, the signal train is negated, logic 1 becoming 0 and logic 0 becoming 1. Hence the output signal will be $\bar{A}$ = 010100.

When A = 101011, B = 110101 are applied to an AND gate, there will be an output (a) only when both inputs are correspondingly (in position) equal to 1. This occurs only as indicated

A = 101011
B = 110101
A.B = 1

The output is then A.B = 100001.

C. FURTHER PROBLEMS ON LOGIC SYMBOLISM

(a) SHORT ANSWER PROBLEMS (answers on page 133)

1 Which switch arrangement gives a truth table corresponding to an AND gate?

2 Which switch arrangement gives a truth table corresponding to an OR gate?

3 When logical 0 is at the input of a certain gate, the output is at logical 1. What gate is this?

4 How many switching combinations are possible with the circuit of *Fig 9*?

5 Write down a logical equation representing the circuit of *Fig 10*.

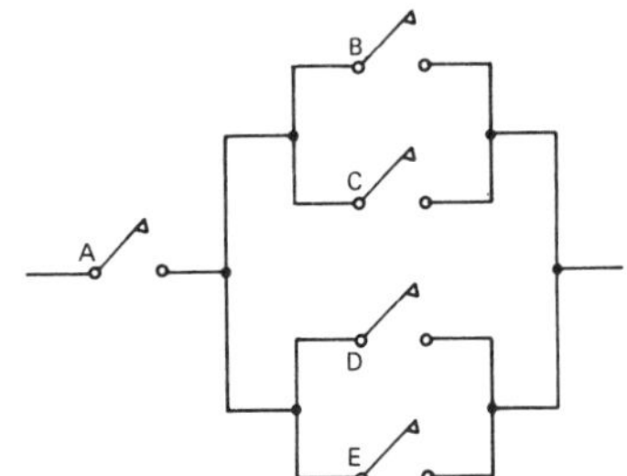

Fig 10

6 Complete the following statements.
(a) The output A + B is provided by a(an) . . . . gate
(b) When logical 0 is at the input of a . . . . gate, the output is logical 1.
(c) An exclusive OR gate will give logical 1 at the output only if A = 1 or B = 1 but not if . . . . is equal to 1.
(d) The + symbol represents the . . . . function
(e) The negation of A is . . . .
(f) The negation of B is . . . .
(g) The logical statement (A and not B) or (B and not A) represents a (an) . . . . gate.

(b) MULTI–CHOICE PROBLEMS (answers on page 133)

1 In positive logic the logic 1 state corresponds to
(a) the higher voltage level;
(b) the lower voltage level;
(c) earth level;
(d) any positive level.

2 In negative logic the logic state 1 corresponds to
(a) the higher voltage level;
(b) the lower voltage level;
(c) earth level;
(d) any negative level.

3 In an AND gate, a logic 1 is obtained at the output when
(a) all inputs are at logic 1;
(b) all inputs are at logic 0;
(c) any one input is at logic 1;
(d) any one input is at logic

4 In an OR gate a logic 1 is obtained at the output when
(a) all inputs are at logic 1;
(b) no inputs are at logic 1;
(c) any one input is at logic 1;
(d) any one input is at logic

5 An input signal A = 10010 is applied to a NOT gate. The output signal is
(a) 10010; (b) 01001; (c) 01101; (d) 00101.

6 Input signals A = 1001, B = 1101 are applied to an AND gate. The signal output will be
(a) 1010; (b) 1001; (c) 0101; (d) 0110.

7 When only signal C is present at the input of a gate represented by the expression F = A.B.C, the output signal is
(a) logic 0 (b) logic 1 (c) dependent upon the logic level used.

8 The table

A	*B*	*F*
0	0	1
0	1	0
1	0	0
1	1	1

represents:
(a) $A + B = F$; (b) $A.B = F$;
(c) $A.B + \bar{A}.\bar{B} = F$; (d) $\bar{A} + \bar{B} = F$.

(c) CONVENTIONAL PROBLEMS

1 What logical functions do the following truth tables represent?

A	*B*	*F*
0	0	0
0	1	0
1	0	0
1	1	1

A	*B*	*F*
0	0	0
0	1	1
1	0	1
1	1	0

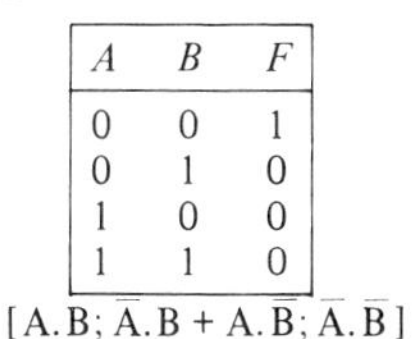

A	*B*	*F*
0	0	1
0	1	0
1	0	0
1	1	0

[$A.B$; $\bar{A}.B + A.\bar{B}$; $\bar{A}.\bar{B}$]

2 Draw switching circuits that will represent the following logical expressions.
(a) $A.B + A.C = F$; (b) $A(B + C)$; (c) $A(\bar{A} + B)$;

3 Use truth tables to verify the following relationships:
(a) $A + B.C = (A + B)\ (A + C)$; (c) $\bar{A} + \bar{B} = \bar{A}.\bar{B}$;
(b) $A(\bar{A} + B) = AB$; (d) $\bar{A}.\bar{B} + A.C + \bar{B}.D = \bar{A} + \bar{B}$.

4 The expression A.B + C.D. applies to one and only one of the switching curcuits shown in *Fig 11*. Which is it?

[(d)]

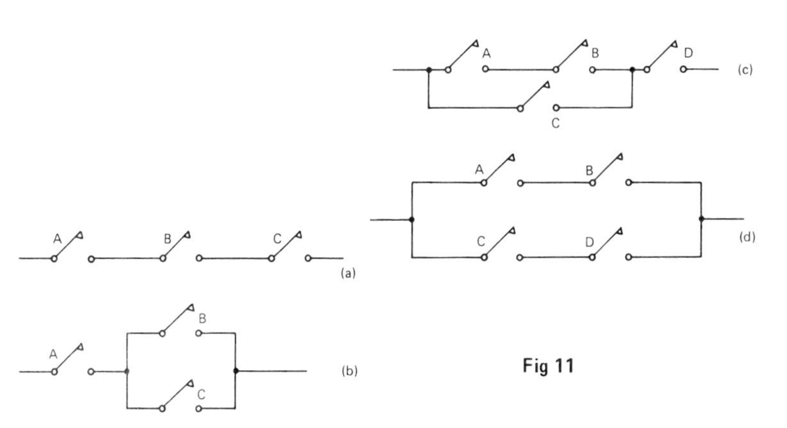

Fig 11

5 The following truth table applies to one and only one of the switching circuits of *Fig 11*. Which is it?

A	B	C	F
0	0	0	0
0	0	1	0
0	1	0	0
0	1	1	0
1	0	0	0
1	0	1	0
1	1	0	0
1	1	1	1

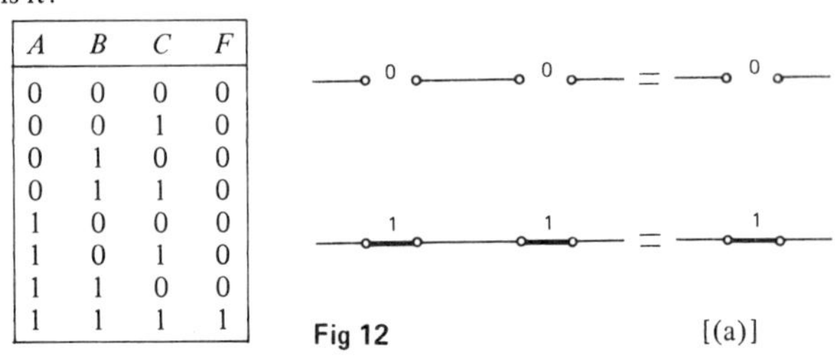

Fig 12

[(a)]

6 The expressions 0.0 = 0 and 1.1 = 1 are illustrated respectively at (a) and (b) in *Fig 13*. Using these as a guide, draw circuit interpretations of
(a) $0 + 0 = 0$;
(b) $1 + 1 = 1$;
(c) $1 + 0 = 1$;
(d) $A + 1 = 1$,
(e) $A + 0 = A$;
(f) $A.0 = 0$,
(g) $A.1 = A$;
(h) $A + \overline{A} = 1$.

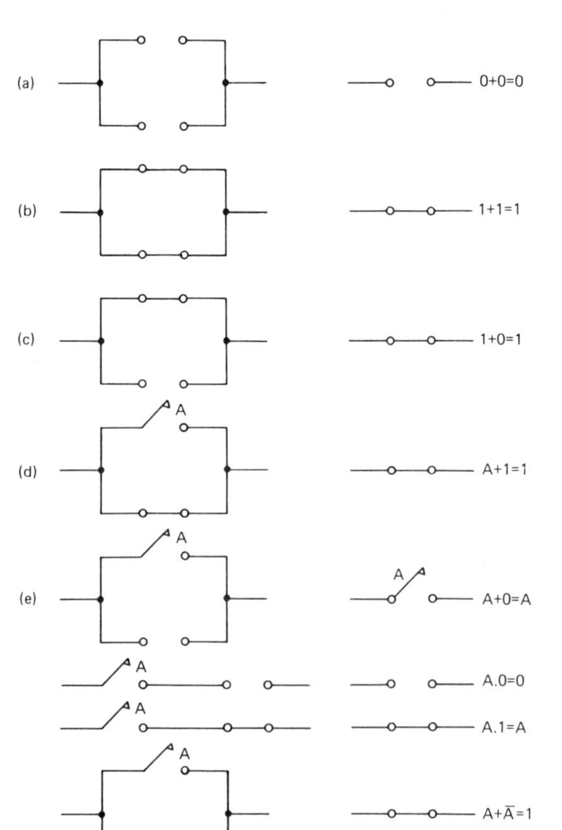

Fig 13

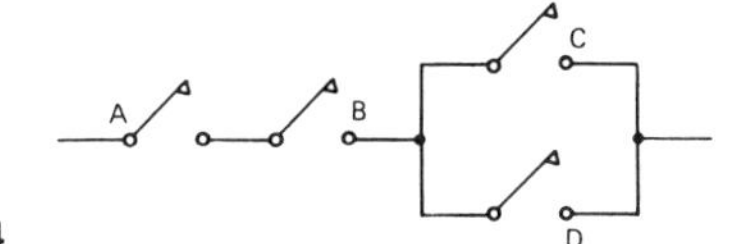

Fig 14

7 Describe, with the aid of waveform sketches, what is meant by postive and negative logic.

8 Describe the action of the circuit shown in *Fig 14* by drawing up a truth table. Write down the logical expression which defines this circuit action.

[A.B (C + D)]

9 Combinational logic gate elements

A. MAIN POINTS CONCERNING COMBINATIONAL LOGIC GATE ELEMENTS

1 So far we have discussed logical relationships and their interpretation in the form of simple switching circuits. In practical terms, it is necessary to have a basic series of logic gate elements that will perform by purely electronic means. There are five basic gates of interest: those covering the three logical functions dealt with in the previous section plus two others which are combinations of these, namely, the NOT-AND or NAND gate and the NOT-OR or NOR gate.

The symbols representing these five gates (plus the X-OR or EXCLUSIVE-OR gate) are given in *Figs 1* and *2*. These are respectively the British Standard (BS)

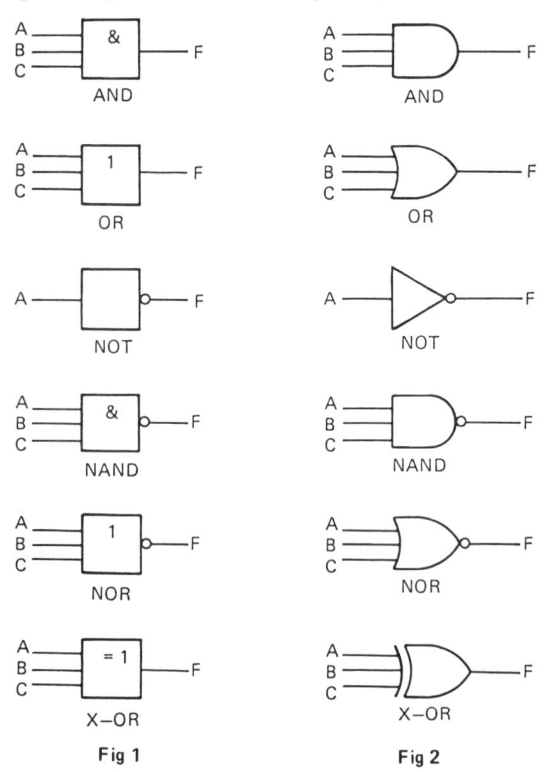

Fig 1

Fig 2

symbols and the ANSI (American) symbols. You should make yourself familiar with both forms. Three inputs have been assigned to these gate symbols, though any number from two upwards may be required in practice. Each gate has one output terminal, designated F. The NOT gate is the exception, having one input and one output terminal only.

So that you can become familiar with both sets of logical symbols, we will use BS in this present chapter and ANSI in a later chapter.

2 Each input signal to these gates will consist of electrical pulses which may represent one or other of two possible states; in general voltage levels are concerned, zero voltage corresponding to logic level 0 and, perhaps, +5 V corresponding to logic level 1. Any two dissimilar voltage levels may be used as input signal representations of logic levels 0 and 1. We shall assume throughout this chapter that positive logic is being used.

3 A great variety of circuits are possible which perform the basic logic functions of AND, OR and NOT and only the simplest will be described here as examples of these circuits. Transistors may be employed in conjunction with diodes forming DTL (diode-transistor-logic) or the diodes may be replaced by a multiple-emitter transistor or integrated circuit form which gives TTL (transistor-transistor-logic) gates. DTL systems are rarely used in practice, but their operation forms an easy approach to an understanding of electronic gate systems in general.

4 The logic AND gate symbolised in *Fig 2* receives a number of input signals, but does not produce an output unless all the inputs are simultaneously present i.e. each input is at a 1 state. The AND gate is often known as a **coincidence gate** for this reason.

A circuit which will operate as an AND gate is shown in *Fig 3*. This circuit uses diodes as the active elements and three input terminals are assumed. In principle any number of inputs might be employed though in practice it is difficult to purchase a gate having more than about 4 inputs. Suppose all inputs are at the high level (logic 1) and that the supply voltage level V is greater than that. Then all the diodes will conduct because their anode voltages are at a higher level than their cathodes. The input signal level (logic 1) therefore is connected directly to the output terminal and so the output is at logic level 1. Replacing the diodes by switches as in *Fig 4(a)* shows this condition.

Now assume that one of the inputs, say A, goes low (logic 0). The cathode of diode A is then low but the anode is high, hence the diode conducts and connects the low input level directly to the output terminal. This has the effect of bringing the anodes of diodes B and C (as well as the output at F) also to the low level. Hence B and C switch off because their cathodes are still at the high logic level 1 but their anodes are low. The output is correspondingly low as the switch analogy of *Fig 4(b)* shows. Using the same reasoning, the output can be shown to be low whenever any two of the inputs are low and the third is high, or all three are low. Only the simultaneous presence of high input levels at all three input terminals produces a high level output.
Hence

A.B.C. = F or 1.1.1 = 1

and the circuit performs as a logical AND gate.

5 The logical OR gate, symbolised in *Fig 2*, provides an output (logic 1) if any one of its inputs is at level 1. It is necessary to distinguish between an inclusive and an exclusive OR gate. Considering a two-input OR gate for simplicity, then if the

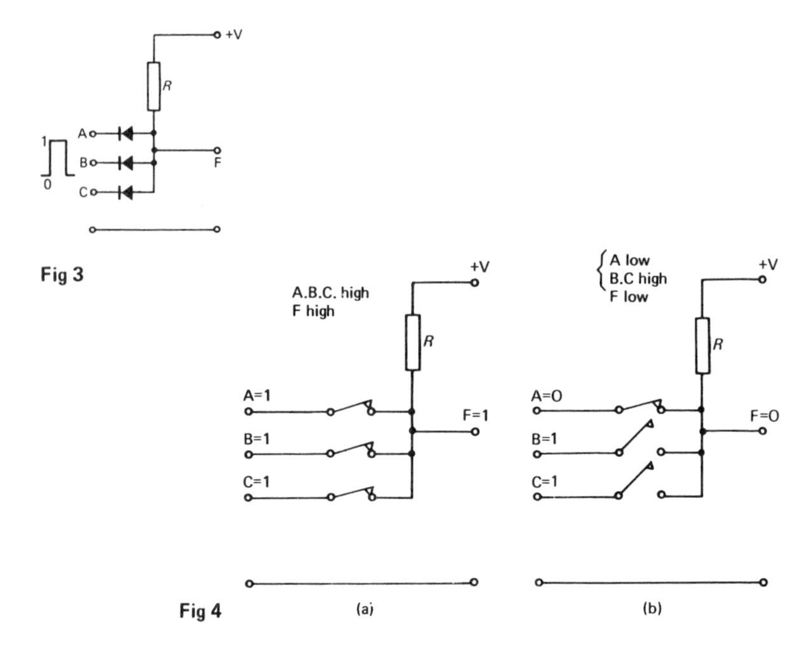

output is 1 when A = 1 or B = 1 or both are 1, the gate is inclusive. If the output is 1 *only* when A = 1 or B = 1 but is 0 when *both* equal 1 the gate is exclusive. The analogy of two (or more) switches in parallel is an inclusive gate. The symbol for the exclusive OR gate is shown in *Fig 2.*

A circuit which will operate as an OR gate is shown in *Fig 5*. Again, diodes are used and three input terminals are assumed. The diode cathodes are returned to a negative voltage level –V. When all the inputs are low (logic 0) all the diodes conduct, their cathodes being negative with respect to their anodes. The input signal level (logic 0) is then connected directly to the output terminal and so the output is at logic 0. Replacing the diodes by switches as in *Fig 6(a)* shows this condition.

Now assume that one of the inputs, say A, goes high (logic 1). The anode of diode A is then high but its cathode is at a negative level, hence the diode conducts and connects the high input level directly to the output terminal. This has the effect of bringing the cathodes of diodes B and C (as well as the output at F) also to the high level. Hence B and C switch off because their anodes are still at the low logic level 0 but their cathodes are high. The output is correspondingly high (logic 1) as the switch analogy of *Fig 6(b)* shows.

Using the same reasoning, the output can be shown to be high whenever any two of the inputs are high and the third is low, or all three are high.
Hence

$A + B + C = F$ and the circuit performs as a logical (inclusive) OR gate.

6 The logical NOT (or negation) function, symbolised in *Fig 2* has one input and one output terminal, and the output is the negation of the input. For an input A,

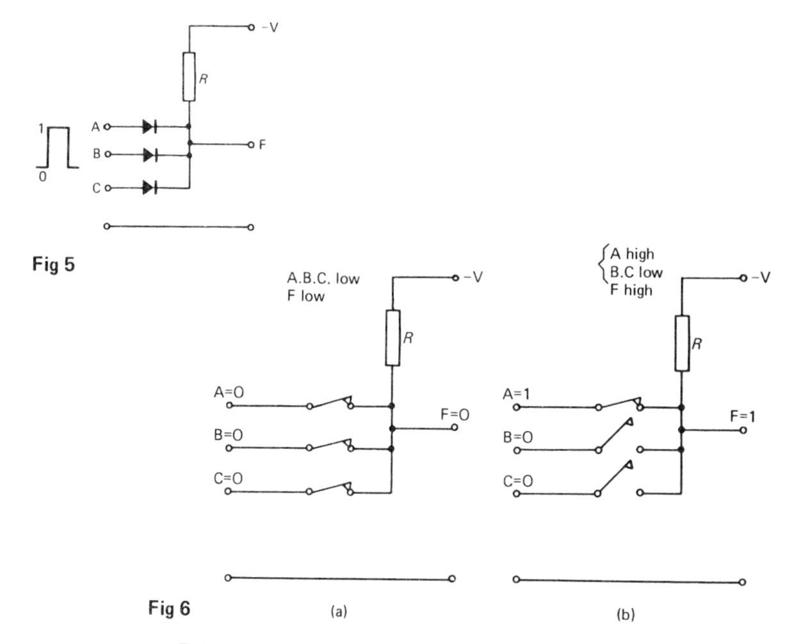

Fig 5

Fig 6 (a) (b)

the output is $\bar{A}$ (not -A) and vice versa, or in the usual logic, the output is 0 when the input is 1, and vice versa. A simple common emitter amplifier circuit will behave as a NOT gate.

A circuit is shown in *Fig 7*. The bias voltage is such that the transistor is initially switched off. The output terminal F is then at the potential of the positive supply rail + V_{CC} since there is no current flow in load resistor R and hence no voltage

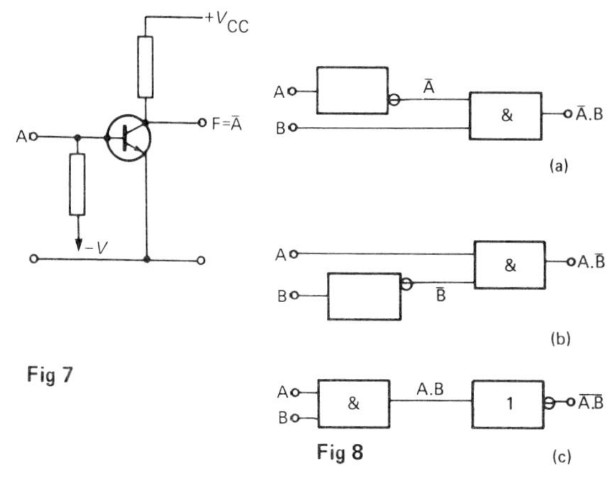

Fig 7

Fig 8 (a) (b) (c)

drop across it. When a high voltage (logic 1) is applied at the base input, the bias voltage is counteracted and the transistor conducts. The output then falls (almost) to zero i.e. logic level 0. The output logic level is always the reverse or negation of the input state, hence the circuit acts as a NOT gate.

7 Logic gates have so far been explained in the form of single elements. Using the three basic gates of AND, OR and NOT, it is possible to make up circuit combinations which represent a great number of logical expressions.

(i) With a two input AND gate and a NOT gate, outputs representing the logical expressions $\bar{A}.B$, $A.\bar{B}$ and $\bar{A}.\bar{B}$ can be obtained. These are shown in *Fig 8*. The outputs can be followed through by considering the intermediate logic states shown arrowed; for example, in diagram (a) input A is inverted to $\bar{A}$ and this together with B forms the input to the AND gate. The final output is then $\bar{A}.B$.

(ii) With a two input OR gate and a NOT gate, outputs representing the logical expressions $\bar{A} + B$, $A + \bar{B}$ and $\overline{A + B}$ can be obtained. *Fig 9* shows these linked elements and the way in which the required output is derived.

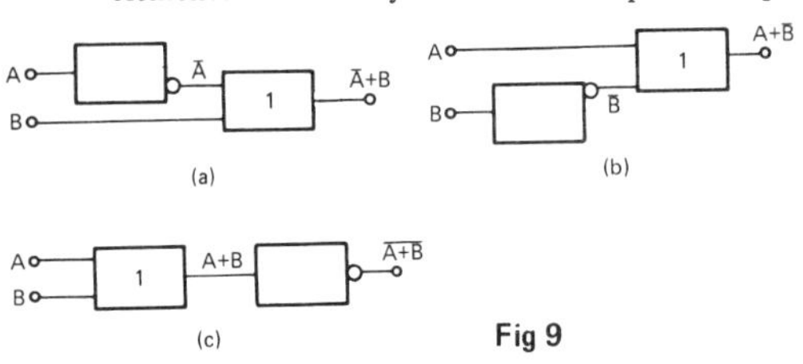

Fig 9

(iii) It is possible to make up systems of AND, OR and NOT gates to produce (a) a NAND or NOT-AND circuit and (b) a NOR or NOT-OR circuit. These gates have very important applications in logical engineering.

The NAND gate is shown in *Fig 10*. It is made up of an AND gate and a NOT gate. When signal A.B from the AND gate is applied to the NOT gate

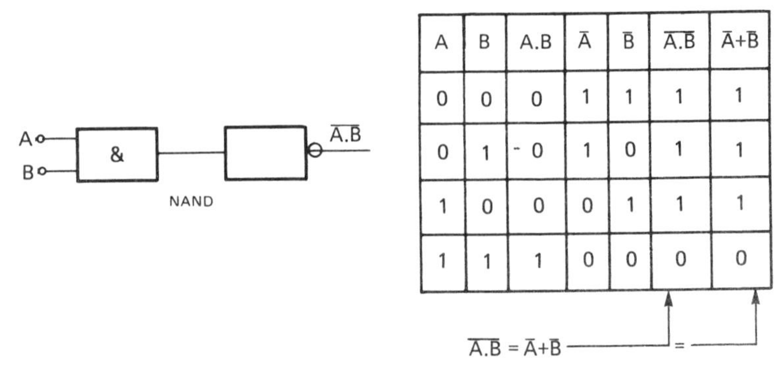

A	B	A.B	$\bar{A}$	$\bar{B}$	$\overline{A.B}$	$\bar{A}+\bar{B}$
0	0	0	1	1	1	1
0	1	0	1	0	1	1
1	0	0	0	1	1	1
1	1	1	0	0	0	0

Fig 10

the output is $\overline{A.B}$. Notice that the negation bar is drawn across both A and B. This means that the NOT gate inverts A to $\bar{A}$, AND to OR, and B to $\bar{B}$.

Hence

$$\overline{A.B.} = \overline{A} + \overline{B}$$

The truth table of *Fig. 10* verifies this statement.

The NOR gate is shown in *Fig 11*. It is made up of an OR gate and a NOT gate. Where this is a signal on one of the inputs or on any combination of the

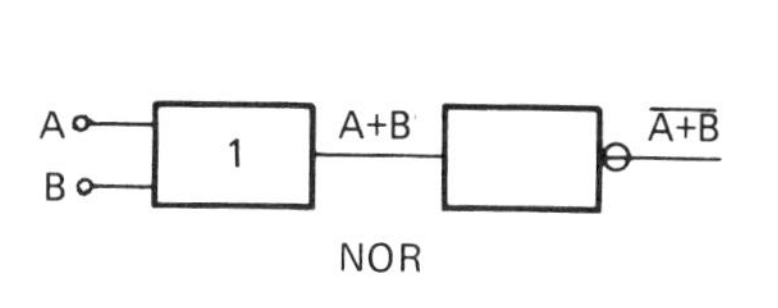

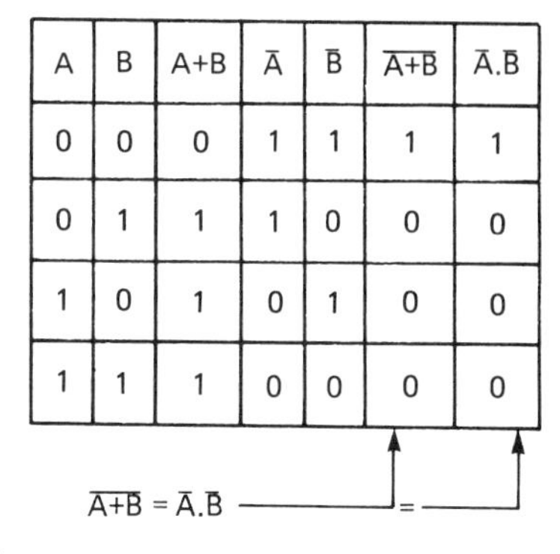

A	B	A+B	$\overline{A}$	$\overline{B}$	$\overline{A+B}$	$\overline{A}.\overline{B}$
0	0	0	1	1	1	1
0	1	1	1	0	0	0
1	0	1	0	1	0	0
1	1	1	0	0	0	0

Fig 11

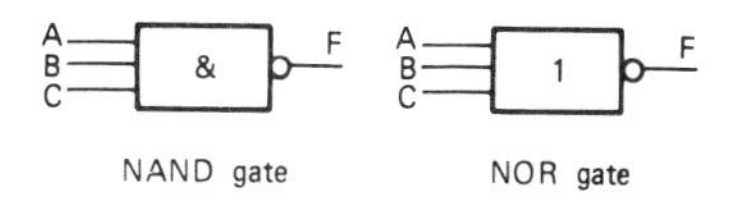

Fig 12

inputs there is a '0' signal at the output. In symbols, $\overline{A} + \overline{B}$. Notice again that the negation bar implies that NOT applies to the whole term. Hence the NOT gate inverts A to $\overline{A}$, OR to AND, and B to $\overline{B}$. From the truth table of *Fig 11* we have

$$\overline{A + B} = \overline{A}.\overline{B}$$

The symbols for the NAND and NOR gate are shown in *Fig 12*.

8 It is not convenient to make up complicated logical systems by connecting together gate circuits made up from discrete component parts, although this is quite satisfactory and instructive for experimental investigations. Such assemblies would be large and unwieldy, difficult to make tests on and consume considerable power. As a consequence, logic gate systems have become available in the form of compact integrated circuit families in the basic forms of the 7400 and 4000 series of packages.

These integrated packages are available at very low cost, each package measuring only a centimeter or so in length and containing a number of identical and individual gates. In a circuit system, one or all of the gates contained in the package may be used. Manufacturers issue data sheets for each of their integrated packages and a number of important parameters such as operating voltage limits and logic input levels must be understood before any such gates are built into a system.

B. WORKED PROBLEMS ON LOGIC GATES

Problem 1 What is the main disadvantage of using diodes and resistors as gate elements and how can this disadvantage be overcome?

Circuits using diodes and resistors have the disadvantage that diodes have a forward voltage drop so that an input logic level of $+V$ volts will give an output that is less than V vol[ts]. Also there is a loss of power in resistor dissipation. If a number of such circuits are used i[n a] complex arrangement, there will be a considerable reduction in the signal level and errati[c] operation may result.

The problem can be resolved by following a diode-resistor circuit with a transistor amplifier as shown in *Fig 13*. Used in this way, the transistor introduces a small voltage drop but the available signal power is increased. When the logic gate feeds into a number of other gates the addition of the transistor is necessary. The number of such gates that can be fed from the output without affecting the performance is known as the **fan-out** of the circuit. In the same way, the number of available inputs is known as the **fan-in**.

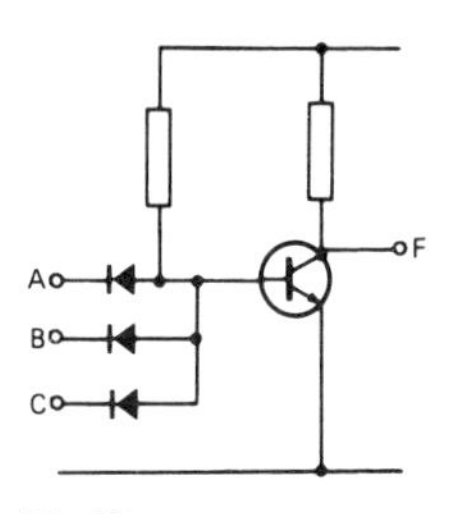

Fig 13

This circuit is, of course, an AND diode gate followed by a transistor inverter or NOT gate. The system therefore represents a NAND gate coming under the general form of a diode-transistor logic or DTL gate.

Problem 2 The DTL gate of *Fig 13* has itself a disadvantage. Explain what this is and how it can be overcome.

If silicon diodes are used in the AND gate part of the circuit, they will have a forward voltage drop of about 0.6 V when conducting. This means that the transistor base will be held at 0.6 V whenever it is supposed to be switched off; this voltage level is such that the transistor is either going to be *just* turned off or not quite turned off. Whichever way it happens to be, the situation is not satisfactory; the transistor has to be firmly turned off when any or all of the input diodes are conducting. The problem can be eased by inserting a **level shifting** diode (sometimes two are used) as shown in *Fig 14*. When one or more inputs are low and point Z is consequently held at 0.6 V, the presence of the level shifting diode(s) now prevents sufficient current flowing into the transistor base to permit it to conduct, hence it switches fully off and the output goes high. Switch-on is unaffected since the level shifting diode is always forward biased.

Problem 3 Devise a circuit made up from AND, OR and NOT elements that will perform the function of the exclusive OR circuit.

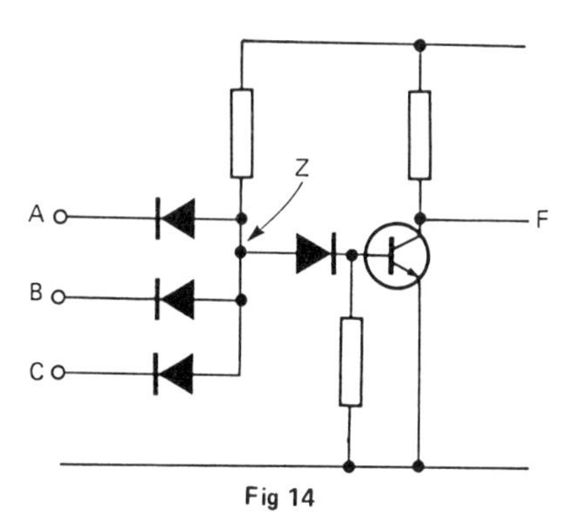

Fig 14

From the truth table for an exclusive OR circuit shown in *Table 7*, Chapter 8 (page 91) the required logical equation is

$$F = (A \text{ and not } B) \text{ or } (B \text{ and not } A)$$
$$= A.\bar{B}. + B.\bar{A}$$

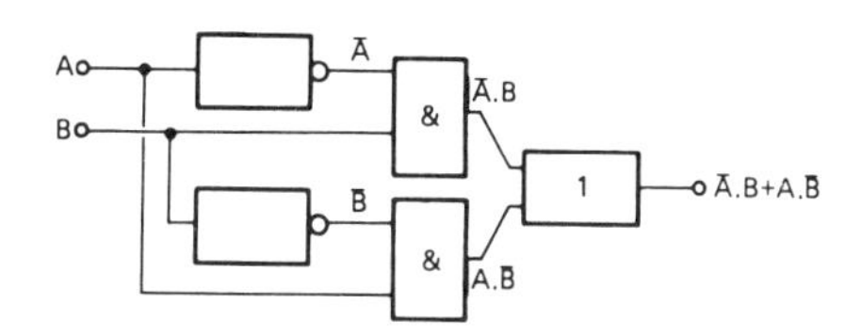

Fig 15

Fig 15 shows the required linking. From the equation, we notice that **A.B̄, B.Ā.** are connected by the OR symbol, hence these two terms are the outputs of an OR gate having the separate inputs A.B̄ and B.Ā. These terms are in turn connected by the AND symbol, so that each is the output of AND gates having respective twin inputs A, B̄ and B, Ā. The negated signals are derived in turn from two NOT gates wired into the input lines as shown. Hence the complete exclusive OR circuit is made up from one OR, two NOT and two AND elements. The OR element itself is an inclusive gate.

The linking together of a number of basic gates to form a given function is known as the **implementation** of that function.

Problem 4 Using only NOR gates, devise circuits representing the basic NOT, AND, and OR elements.

One of the reasons why the NOR (and the NAND) elements are important is that all other gates can be implemented from them. *Fig 16(a)* shows how the NOT gate can be implemented for a NOR element using only one of its inputs. The NOR then inverts exactly as does a NOT. In *Fig 16(b)* the AND gate is implemented from three NOR elements, by a process of double negation. In diagram (c) two NOR elements implement the OR function, again by double negation.

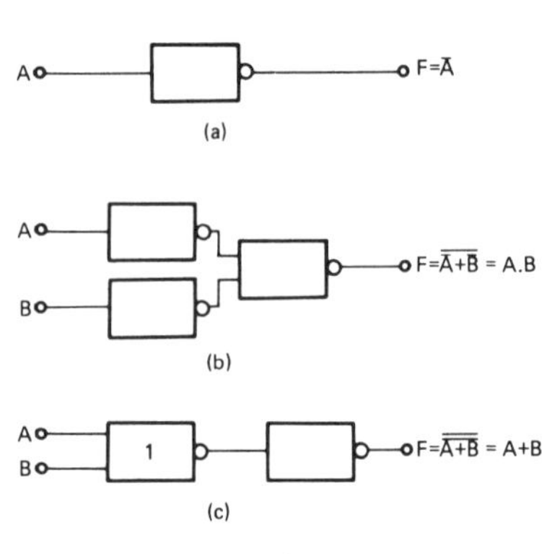

Fig 16

Problem 5 Design a logical system of gate elements for the control of a machine which cannot be started until:
(a) the starter button is pressed; (b) the machine guard is closed; (c) the coolant is on; but which must stop if (d) the stop button is pressed; (e) the guard is opened, (f) the coolant fails; (g) the machine overloads.

On consideration, conditions (a), (b) and (c) are connected by the AND function. The machine clearly must not start until the starter button is pressed AND the guard is closed AND the coolant is on. An output will be obtained from a three-input AND gate when these conditions are simultaneously established at the input. Condition (d) to (g) must be connected with the OR and NOT functions. The machine must stop

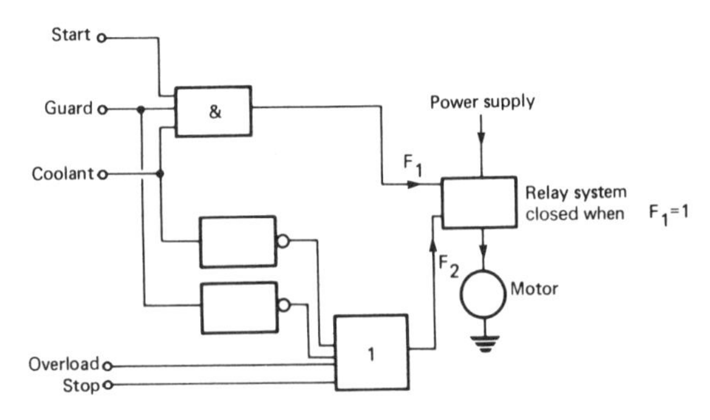

Fig 17

if the stop button is pressed OR the guard is opened OR the coolant fails OR the machine overloads. As the guard and coolant are associated with the AND set of conditions as well as the OR set, NOT gates must be included in the feed from these control signal points to the OR gate. Strictly then, we have NOR conditions here.

A system fulfilling the above conditions is shown in *Fig 17*. A simplification is possible here – can you see what it is?

Problem 6 What effect would the application of negative logic signals have on the AND gate illustrated in *Fig 18*?

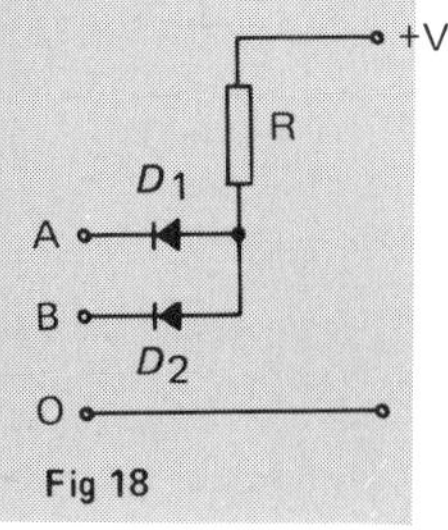

Fig 18

Using positive logic, when A and B are at 0 V, the output is 0 V. If A goes to, say, +5 V, D_2 still conducts and keeps the output at 0 V, which reverse biases D_1. Similarly, if B goes to +5 V while A is still at O V, the output still remains at 0 V and D_2 is non-conducting. When both inputs go to +5 V, both diodes conduct and the output goes to 5 V. For negative logic, when A and B are at 0 V, the output is at 0 V, exactly as before. If now A goes to say, −5 V instantaneously both diodes would conduct. When D_2 is conducting, however, the output is at 0 V, which still leaves D_1 forward biased. Therefore D_1 conducts and puts the output at −5 V, i.e. logic 1. This cuts off D_2 since its cathode is at 0 V and its anode is at −5 V. Similarly, if B goes to −5 V while A is still at 0 V, the output is put at −5 V and D_1 is cut off. When both A and B go to −5 V both diodes conduct and the output is again at −5 V. If we look at the truth table for negative logic, it is as in *Table 1*.

TABLE 1

A	*B*	*F*
0	0	0
0	1	1
1	0	1
1	1	1

This is the truth table for the OR function. Therefore, the circuit in question performs the AND function for positive logic or in the OR function for negative logic. In the same way, the circuit of *Fig 5* which performs the OR function for positive logic will perform the AND function for negative logic.

C. FURTHER PROBLEMS ON LOGIC GATE ELEMENTS

(a) SHORT ANSWER PROBLEMS (ASSUME POSITIVE LOGIC THROUGHOUT)

(answers on page 134)

1 Complete the following:

(a) A logic 1 is obtained from an .... gate if and only if all of the inputs are at logic 1.

(b) If one of four inputs to an OR gate is logical 1, the output is logical ....

(c) The output from a NOT gate is the .... of the input signal.

(d) A DTL gate is a gate using .... and ....

(e) A NAND gate is a(an) .... gate and .... gate in series

(f) A NOR circuit contains both .... and .... elements
(g) A NOR gate with a single input is equivalent to a(an) .... gate
(h) If input A to a two-input NAND gate is logical 1 and input B is logical 0, the output F = ...
(i) A positive logic AND gate is equivalent to a negative logic .... gate.

2 Say whether the following statements are true or false:
(a) In an AND gate a logic 0 output is obtained when
 (i) All inputs are at logic 0
 (ii) No inputs are at logic 0
 (iii) Any one input is at logic 0
(b) In an OR gate a logic 1 output is obtained when
 (i) all inputs are at logic 1
 (ii) no inputs are at logic 1
 (iii) any one input is at logic 1
(c) A two-input exclusive OR gate gives logic 1 as output if
 (i) A = 1 and B = 1
 (ii) A = 1 and B = 0
 (iii) A = 0 and B = 1
 (iv) A = 0 and B = 0
(d) Two inputs A and B are applied to a NOR gate. The output expression will be
 (i) $F = \overline{A} + B$
 (ii) $F = A + \overline{B}$
 (iii) $F = \overline{A + B}$
 (iv) $F = \overline{A} + \overline{B}$
(e) A NAND gate followed by a NOT gives an overall equivalent to
 (i) an AND gate; (ii) an OR gate; (iii) a NOR gate.

3 *Fig 19* represents a circuit in a box. Each of the terminals ABC and D can have potentials of either O V or 5 V. When A,B and C are at 5 V, D is also at 5 V. When one or more of the inputs is at 0 V, D is also at 0 V. What circuit is in the box?

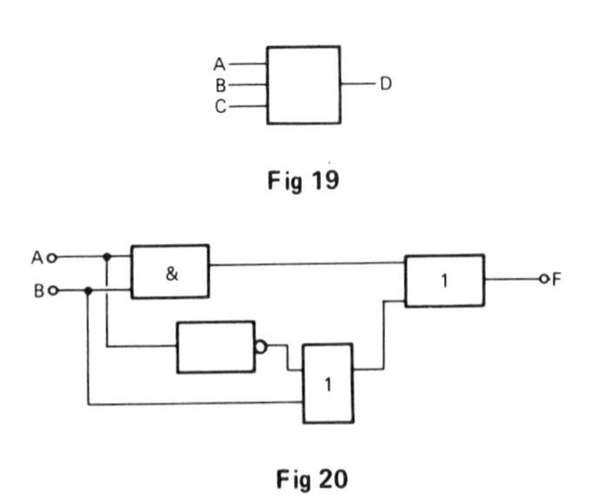

Fig 19

Fig 20

4 An input signal A = 011010110 is applied to the input of a NOT gate. Write down the output signal.

5 Input signals A = 1010001, B = 1000111 are applied to the input of an AND gate. Write down the output signal.

6 Input signals A = 101011, B = 100100 are applied to the input terminals of the logic system shown in *Fig 20*. What is the output signal at F?

7 Sketch logic diagrams, using AND and OR elements only, implementing the function

(a) F = A.B + C;
(b) F = A.B + C.D,
(c) F = A.B + $\overline{C}$,
(d) F = A + A.B;
(e) F = C(A + B).

(b) CONVENTIONAL PROBLEMS

1 What types of logic circuit are needed to represent the logical expressions (a) A.B.C = F; (b) A + B + C = F; (c) $\overline{A}$ = F. Draw a truth table for each case and sketch the symbol for the individual gates.

[(a) AND; (b) OR; (c) NOT]

2 Sketch two circuits using diodes and resistors which will perform the functions of (a) and (b) in the previous problem.

[see *Figs 3 and 5*]

3 Write down the logical equations representing the output of the circuits shown in *Fig 21*. By the use of truth tables, verify that both circuits perform in the same logical function. What fact of importance does this example illustrate?

[Complicated circuits can often be simplified]

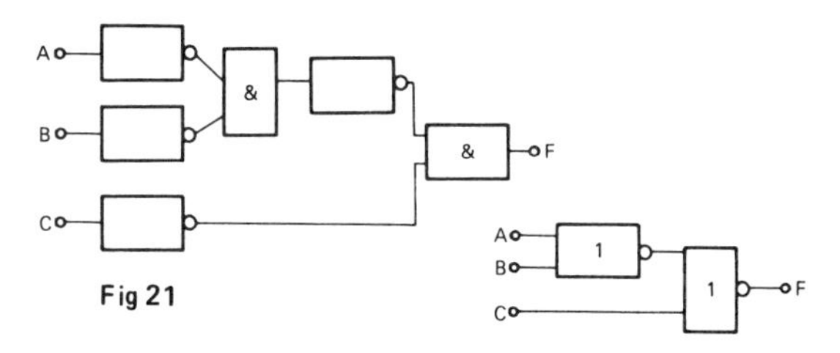

Fig 21

4 Sketch the output voltage waveforms obtained from the diode gates of *Fig 22(a)* when the input signal waveforms shown against each gate are applied at the appropriate terminals.

[see *Fig 22(b)*]

Fig 22(a)

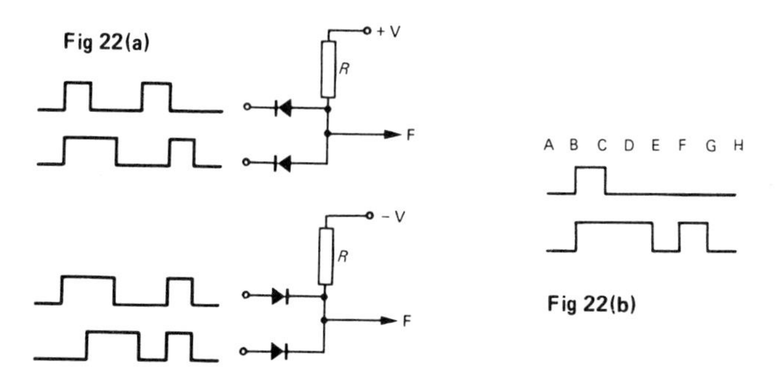

Fig 22(b)

5 In the circuits of *Fig 23* the input logic levels are: logic 0 = 0 V; logic 1 = +5 V.
(a) Under what condition(s) will the potential at X be +5 V?
(b) What then will be the potential at Y?
(c) What logic function does this circuit perform?

[(a) When either A or B is at +5 V
(b) About zero; (c) NOR]

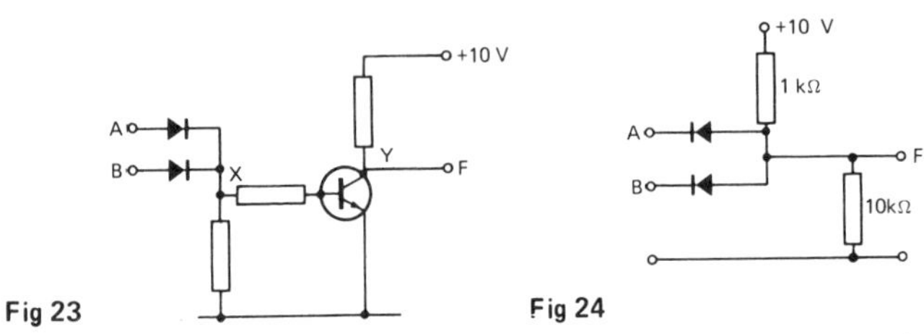

Fig 23 Fig 24

6 In the two-input AND circuit of *Fig 24* the input logic levels are 0 V (O) and + 10 (1). What is the voltage at F when A and B are both at logic 1 and the output is loaded with 10 kΩ?

[9.1 V]

7 *Fig 25* shows a logic system using four gates. State the logic function of each gate and deduce (a) the output F_1 from gate 1; (b) the output F_2 from gate 2; (c) the final output F, when the input signals are A = 101001, B = 110011.

[(a) 111011; (b) 100001; (c) 000100]

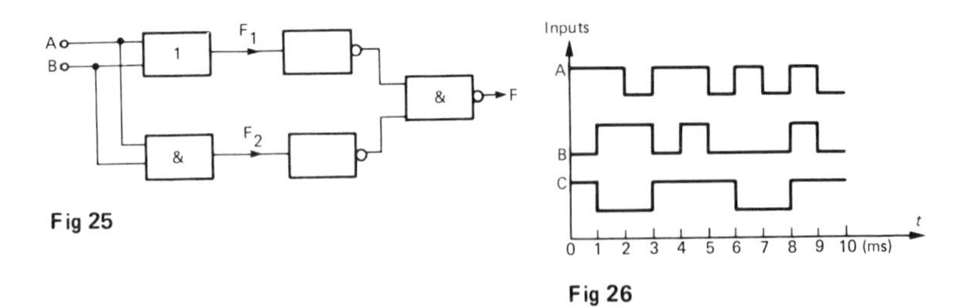

Fig 25

Fig 26

8 *Fig 26* shows a train of input pulses A, B and C which are applied in turn to a three-input (i) AND gate; (ii) inclusive OR gate; (iii) exclusive OR gate. The time scale indicates millisecaids of duration. Between what times are there outputs from (a) the AND gate; (b) the inclusive OR gate (C) the exclusive OR gate?

[(a) 4–5 and 8–9 mS; (b) 0.7 and 8–10 ms;
(c) 2–3, 5–7, 9–10 mS]

9 Devise a circuit using only AND, OR and NOT elements whose output will represent the logical function $F = (\bar{A} + B) C$

[See *Fig 27*]

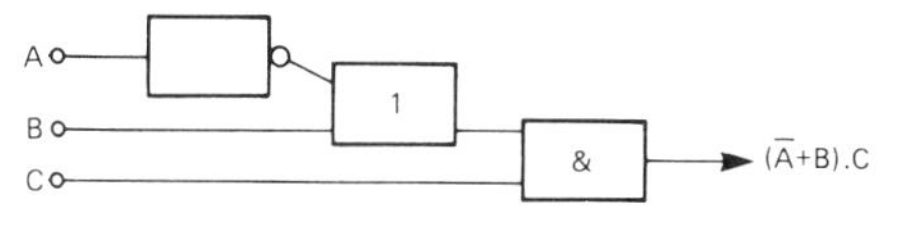

Fig 27

10 Explain the difference between the expressions $F = \overline{A.B}$ and $\overline{A}.\overline{B}$. Sketch two gate circuits, having inputs A and B, which would produce these outputs.

11 Draw a truth table for the expression $F = A + A.B$. Compare this table with the statement $F = A$. What do you conclude?

[Identical expressions]

12 Draw logic diagrams implementing the functions
(i) $F = A.B + C$;
(ii) $F = A.B + C.D$;
(iii) $F = A.B + C$;
(iv) $F = C(A+B)$

[See *Fig 28*]

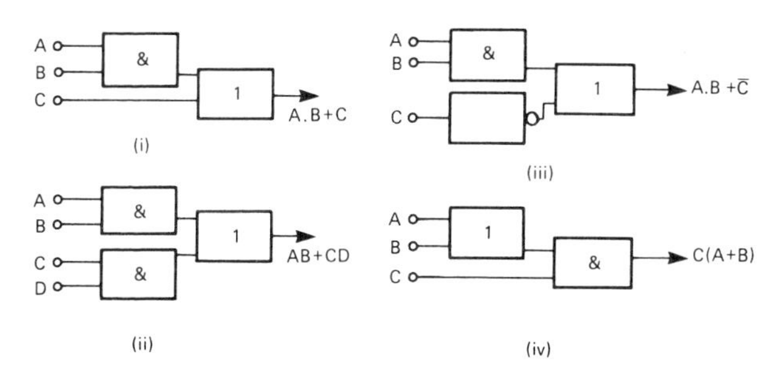

Fig 28

13 Using only NAND elements, implement (as in *Problem 4* earlier) the basic NOT, AND and OR elements.

[See *Fig 29*]

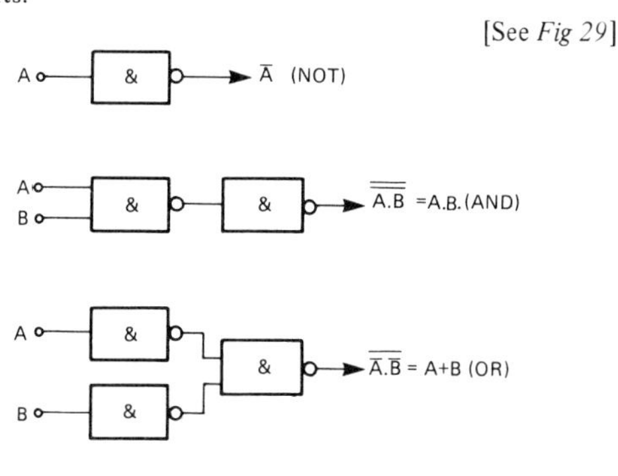

Fig 29

14 A machine operator controls red and green indicator lights by four switches, A, B, C and D. The operating sequence is as follows:
(a) Red light is ON when switch A is ON and switch B is OFF or switch C is ON.
(b) Green light is ON when switches A and B are ON and switches C and D are OFF.
Write down logical expressions representing the conditions (a) and (b) and draw logical circuits illustrating these expressions.

[(a) $A(\overline{B} + C)$; (b) $A.B.\overline{C}.\overline{D}$.]

15 A person is entitled to apply for a certain job if they are
(a) a woman over the age of 40; (b) a married man.
Three switches are provided to test the entitlement:
Switch A puts logical 1 on the output if the person is over 40.
Switch B puts logical 1 on the output if the person is male.
Switch C puts logical 1 on the output if the person is married.
Write down a logical equation for an output F which indicates entitlement and draw a suitable arrangement of gates which would perform this function.

[See *Fig 30*]

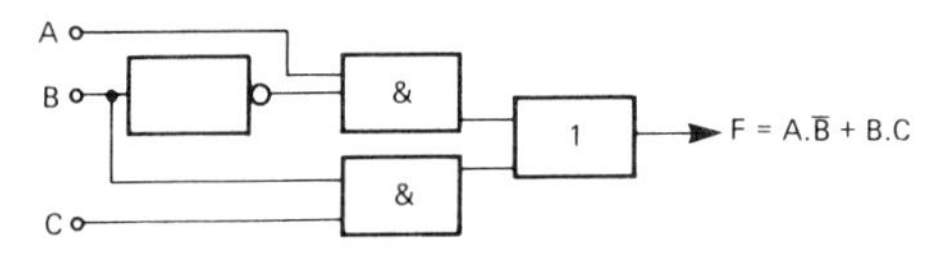

Fig 30

16 A security firm wishes to increase its security by using three door keys, one held by the manager, one by the assistant manager and one by the chief security officer. Design a circuit system which will enable the door to be opened by using any *two* of the keys. Additionally, the main safe is to be opened only by the use of all three keys.

What modification would be fitted so that the door automatically closes whenever the safe is opened?

[See *Fig 31*]

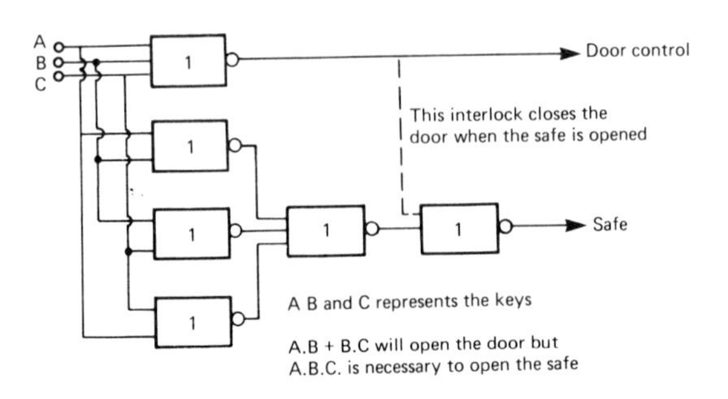

Fig 31

10 Karnaugh mapping

A. MAIN POINTS CONCERNING KARNAUGH MAPS

1 In creating a circuit to perform a particular logical function, a designer clearly wants to go for the most economical way of building up that circuit from the basic gate units at his disposal. The smaller the number of gates needed and the smaller the diversity of types used, the better the design. In **minimising** a given logical system in this way, the designer makes use of the fact that a logical expression can often be simplified to give a shorter, neater form of the equation. This simplified interpretation then leads to a simplified circuit system.

2 Karnaugh mapping (or K-mapping) is named after its originator, Maurice Karnaugh, and is a compact graphical way of displaying logical functions or truth tables. In a function having N variables, there are 2^N ways of combining the variables. So we can construct a two-dimensional diagram having a square (or cell) for each possible combination of the input variables. An example for a function of two variables is shown in *Fig 1*. This has four cells since $2^2 = 4$, and each cell within the map is at the intersection of an externally indicated row and column. Each cell thus has a unique address which is defined completely by the label attached to the row or column which intersects at that particular cell. In *Fig 1* the four cells have been given addresses. Notice that the address of any cell differs by no more than one variable from the address of any *adjacent* cell. Diagonal cells are *not* adjacent cells.

3 Karnaugh maps are not usually labelled in the way indicated in *Fig 1*. It is more customary to insert the logic levels (0 or 1) around the perimeter with the variables (A,B,C etc) indicated at the top left-hand corner as shown in *Fig 2*. This makes it a simple matter to map directly from a truth table because each cell in the map corresponds to a row in the truth table.

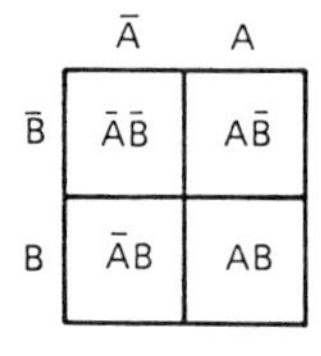

Fig 1

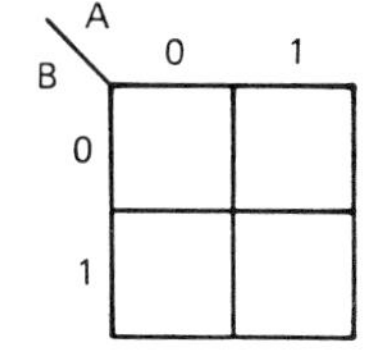

Fig 2

4 A Karnaugh map for a function of three variables is shown in *Fig 3*. In this case it illustrates the action of a three input AND gate – the result is 1 only when all three inputs, A, B and C, are 1. Any function represented in this way on the map can be recognised by the total map area marked by 1s. If a map had all its cells marked by 1s, the function corresponding to it would display unity transmission for all possible combinations of the variables, that is, the relevant logical circuit would give a 1

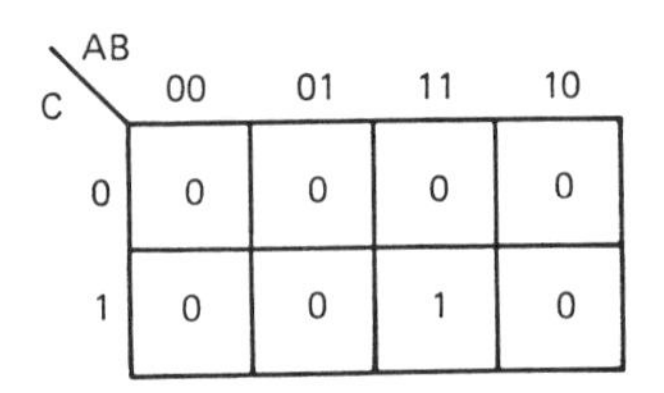

Fig 3

output irrespective of any combinations of its inputs, and would behave as a permanently closed circuit. A map having all cells marked 0 would likewise represent a permanently open circuit, with output 0 for any input combination. Such circuits would have little use in practice!

5 The sequence of 0s and 1s along the sides of a map are often conveniently set out in the cyclic order 00, 01, 10 and 11. It is helpful, however, to get used to working (as we shall in this book) with the order 00, 01, 11, 10, because this is the Gray code sequence which you may well study in later work. The use of the map is not affected in any way by this convention at this stage.

B. WORKED PROBLEMS ON KARNAUGH MAPPING

Problem 1 Draw Karnaugh maps for (a) a two-input OR gate, (b) a two-input NAND gate, working from truth tables.

(a) From the truth table for the OR gate shown in *Fig 4*, F = 1 when A = 1 or B = 1 or both A and B = 1. The Karnaugh mapping shown on the right immediately follows.

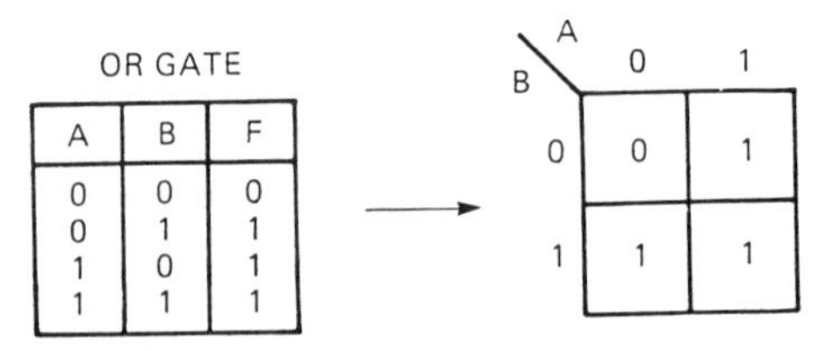

OR GATE

A	B	F
0	0	0
0	1	1
1	0	1
1	1	1

Fig 4

(b) From the truth table for the NAND gate, F = 0 only if A = 1 and B = 1. Again, the map can be immediately filled in as shown on the right in *Fig 5*.

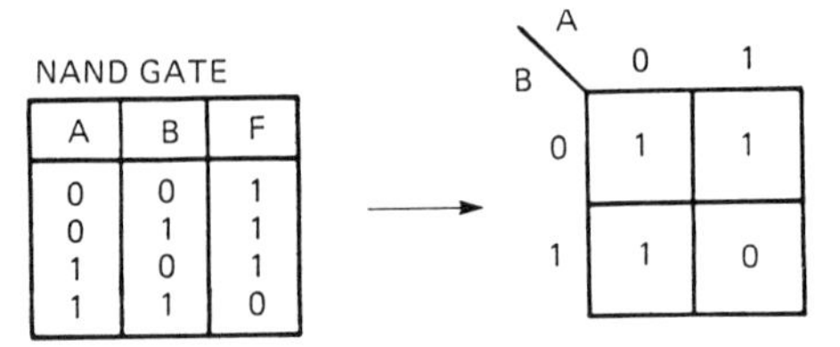

NAND GATE

A	B	F
0	0	1
0	1	1
1	0	1
1	1	0

Fig 5

Problem 2 State which of the following pairs of cells (if any) are adjacent on a Karnaugh map:

(a) $\bar{A}B\bar{C}\bar{D}$, $AB\bar{C}D$ (b) $\bar{A}BC\bar{D}$, $\bar{A}\bar{B}CD$ (c) $AB\bar{C}D$, $A\bar{B}\bar{C}D$

In (a) the terms differ in both the A and D variables; hence these cells are not adjacent.

In (b) the terms differ in both B and D variables; hence these cells are not adjacent.

In (c) the terms differ in only the B variable; hence these cells are adjacent.

Problem 3 The truth table for a three-variable logic circuit is shown in *Fig 6*. Use this table to map the logical equation it represents.

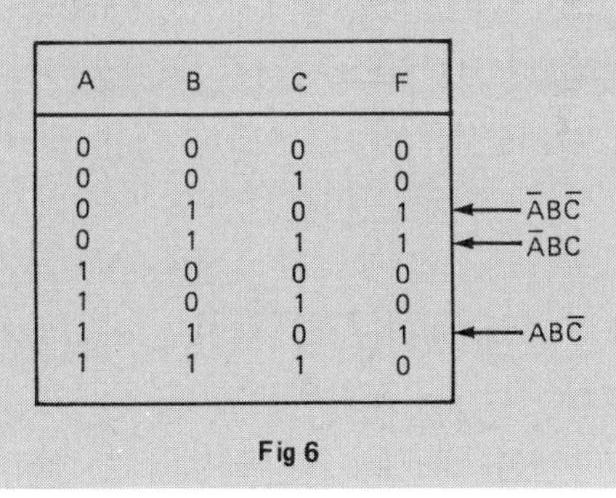

A	B	C	F
0	0	0	0
0	0	1	0
0	1	0	1
0	1	1	1
1	0	0	0
1	0	1	0
1	1	0	1
1	1	1	0

Fig 6

As for *Problem 1* above, we are going to map the truth table, but as an exercise we first deduce the logical equation itself. This is done by taking out those rows of the table where the output F is logical 1. From the indicated rows we get:

$$F = \bar{A}B\bar{C} + \bar{A}BC + AB\bar{C}$$

As there are three variables, we require an eight cell map ($2^3 = 8$). This is shown in *Fig 7*. A 1 is placed in each cell corresponding to the three terms in the logical equation, namely $\bar{A}B\bar{C}$, $\bar{A}BC$ and $AB\bar{C}$. All other cells are marked with 0. The actual terms have been added for illustration and are not normally shown.

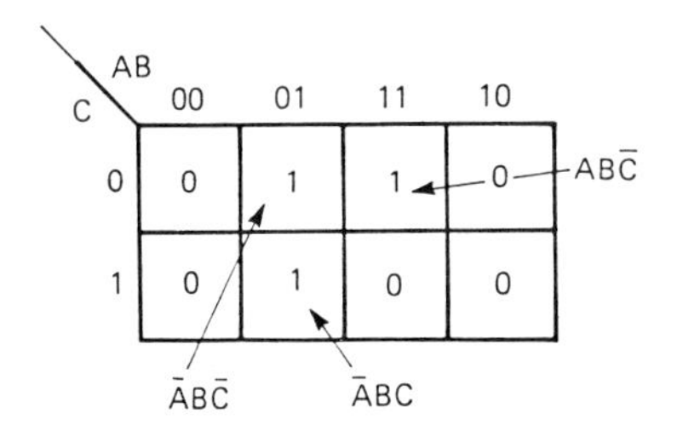

Fig 7

Problem 4 Show that a pair of adjacent cells may be combined on a K-map and described by a function which is independent of that variable across whose boundary the cells are adjacent.

Each cell in a Karnaugh map represents a product of terms, for example, ABC. This is known as a **miniterm.** If there is a 1 in two adjacent cells (for example the cells indicated in *Fig 8*), we notice that the output is 1 for AB and $\overline{A}B$. These differ, of course, by only one variable (the A variable) and so may be combined into a single term B, since $AB + \overline{A}B = B(A + \overline{A})$ which equals B.

This example shows us that we may link any two adjacent cells both containing 1 and replace this pair of cells by the logic variable common to the row or column in which they are found. Or, to put it another way, any pair of adjacent cells may be combined and described by a function *independent* of that variable across whose boundary they are adjacent.

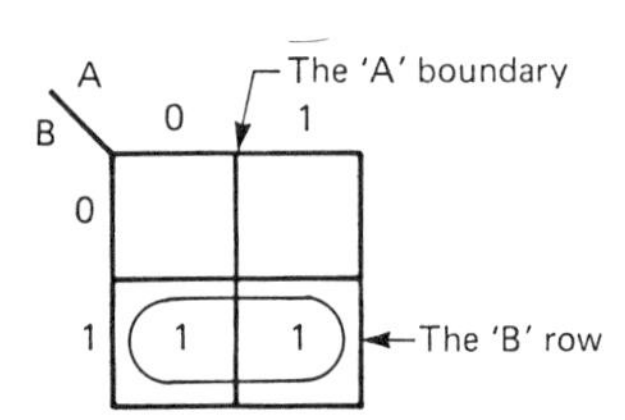

Fig 8

Problem 5 Use a Karnaugh map and the linking of adjacent cells as necessary to show that the logical equation $\overline{A}\overline{B}C + \overline{A}BC + ABC + A\overline{B}C = C$.

The equation given has been plotted as a set of four cells marked in the map of *Fig 9*. You will notice that all four cells have been linked since they are all adjacent to each other. However, working on them in pairs, from $\overline{A}\overline{B}C$, $\overline{A}BC$ we see that these are adjacent across the B boundary, hence their logical sum is independent of the B variable and so:

$$\overline{A}\overline{B}C + \overline{A}BC = \overline{A}C$$

The remaining pair of terms, ABC, $A\overline{B}C$, are adjacent across the B boundary also, and hence reduce to AC.

But the pairs themselves are also adjacent to each other across the A boundary, hence $\overline{A}C + AC$ reduces to C, as required.

What we learn from this example is that four-cell groups are independent of *two* variables, just as two cell groups are independent of one variable. The process of combining cells in this way is the fundamental operation in the use of the Karnaugh map in minimising a logical function.

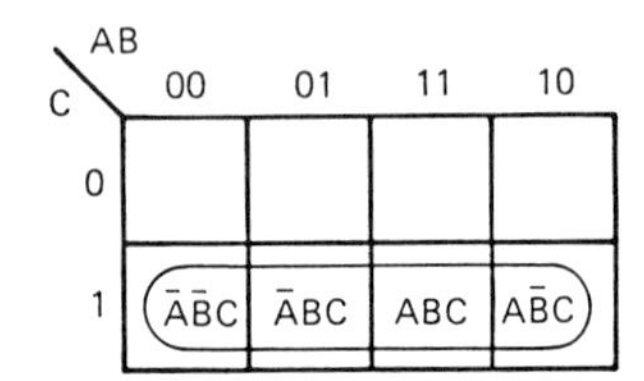

Fig 9

Problem 6 In *Fig 10*, the cells marked $\overline{A}\,\overline{B}\,\overline{C}$ and $A\overline{B}\,\overline{C}$ are, according to our definition, adjacent cells since they differ in only one variable. How does this fact affect the pairing of cells when minimising a function?

A look at any Karnaugh map will show us that the outer boundaries are only *single* boundaries so that, to take the present example, going from $\overline{A}\,\overline{B}\,\overline{C}$ to $A\overline{B}\,\overline{C}$ not only involves crossing the A boundary but entails shifting out of the map entirely, as *Fig 10* illustrates. In other words, the outer boundaries of any map are equivalent. The outer limits of a map may therefore be regarded as being connected together, top to bottom and side to side.

Cells on the boundaries may therefore be combined in the way the diagram shows; in this case, $\overline{A}\,\overline{B}\,\overline{C}$ and $A\overline{B}\,\overline{C}$ are adjacent across the A boundary and so may be combined in the single terms $\overline{B}\,\overline{C}$.

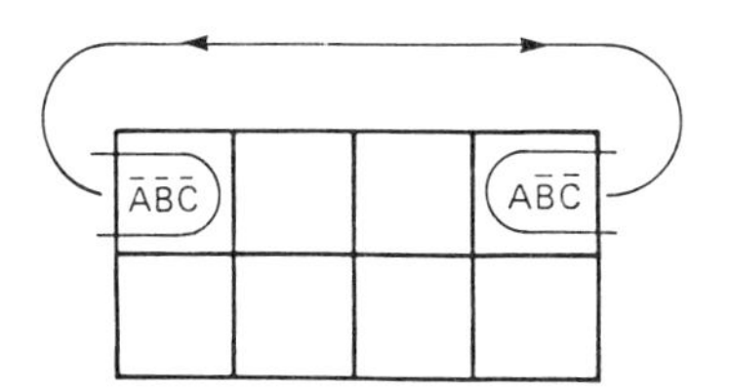

Fig 10

Problem 7 Outline the rules for using the K-map as a minimiser of logical functions.

We assume that the function has been assembled into a normal sum-of-products terms or is available in the form of a truth table. The steps to be taken can then be summarised as follows:

(a) Set up the K-map grid in the form of four, eight or sixteen cells and enter the function as already described.
(b) Examine the map for single (isolated) 1s; pairs of 1s which cannot be included in a larger group; groupings of four 1s (which may include other previously looped as well as unlooped 1s); and group them after the manner shown in *Fig 11*. All the 1s must be finally grouped in this way with no left-overs.

Now write out the logical product terms for each of the loops formed.

Finally, OR these product terms to obtain the minimised expression in sum-of-products form.

Problem 8 Map the function $F = AB + \overline{B}\,\overline{C} + A\overline{B}$ and show that it will minimise to $F = A + \overline{B}\,\overline{C}$.

There are three variables involved so we need an 8-cell map. This is shown in *Fig 10*. The three given terms AB, $\overline{B}\,\overline{C}$ and $A\overline{B}$ might seem at first to present a difficulty as all the cells have addresses involving three variables, and each term contains only two. There is no problem, however, if we notice that the *area* covered by the term AB is that area where A and B *overlap*, that is, it comprises *two* adjacent cells. Individually, these two

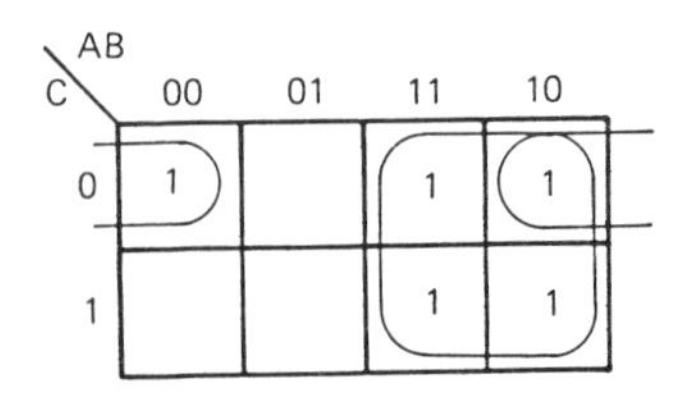

Fig 11

cells are ABC and $AB\overline{C}$ which combine (in the way we did earlier) to produce AB. The term AB, then, is represented by the two cells of the third *column*. In the same way the term $\overline{B}\,\overline{C}$ is represented by the two *outermost* cells of the top row where $\overline{B}$ and $\overline{C}$ overlap; and the term $A\overline{B}$ occupies the two cells of the right-hand *column*. The diagram shows these groupings and the linkages.

Looking at this we see that the 4-cell cluster crosses the B and C boundaries and is contained within the A address zone. Hence it represents just the term A. For the split 2-cell grouping, this crosses the A (edge) boundary and is contained in the $\overline{B}$ and $\overline{C}$ zone. Hence it represents just the term $\overline{B}\,\overline{C}$.

The original function therefore minimises to $F = A + \overline{B}\,\overline{C}$.

C FURTHER PROBLEMS ON KARNAUGH MAPPING

(a) SHORT ANSWER PROBLEMS (answers on page 134)

1. How many cells are required on a K-map to accommodate a four-variable logical function?
2. Are the four corner cells of the previous map adjacent cells? Is this so for any map?
3. What is the miniterm of a logical function?
4. Explain the principle behind the row and column numbering in a Karnaugh map.
5. Do the cells of a Karnaugh map represent miniterms?
6. Which of the following groups, if any, represent adjacent cells: (a) $A\overline{B}C$, ABC; (b) $\overline{A}B\overline{C}$, $AB\overline{C}$, (c) $\overline{A}B\overline{C}D$, $\overline{A}\,\overline{B}C\overline{D}$?
7. Sketch a K-map for an exclusive two-input OR gate.
8. Go back to *Fig 7* and show that the map represents the logical equation $\overline{A}B + B\overline{C}$.

(b) CONVENTIONAL PROBLEMS

1. Map the following logical expressions and find the minimal sum-of-products for each of them:

(a) $ABC + AB\overline{C}$ [AB]
(b) $\overline{A}B + BC + AC$ [$AC + \overline{A}B$]
(c) $\overline{A}BC + AB\overline{C} + ABC$ [AB + BC]
(d) $\overline{A}BC + ABC + A\overline{C}$ [A + B]
(e) $\overline{A}\,\overline{B}C + \overline{A}BC + \overline{A}B\overline{C} + AB\overline{C}$ [$\overline{A}C + B\overline{C}$]
(f) $\overline{A}\,\overline{C} + B\overline{C} + \overline{A}BC + ABC$ [$B + \overline{A}\,\overline{C}$]

2. From the Karnaugh map of *Fig 12*, write down the logical miniterms represented by the cell groupings P, Q, R and S. [$P = B\overline{C}$, $Q = A\overline{B}\,\overline{C}$, $R = C$, $S = \overline{A}\,\overline{B}\,\overline{C}D$]

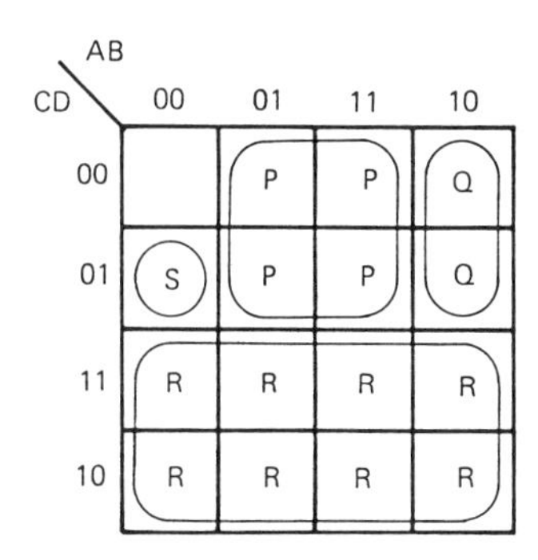

Fig 12

3 Using the truth table given in *Fig 13*, write down the logical expression at the output in sum-of-product form. Use a K-map to simplify this expression and design a circuit using AND, OR and NOT gates which will implement this output. [$\bar{A}\bar{B} + ABC$]

A	B	C	D	F
0	0	0	0	1
0	0	0	1	1
0	0	1	0	1
0	0	1	1	1
1	1	1	0	1
1	1	1	1	1

All other combinations give F = 0

Fig 13

4 Use a K-map to simply the expression $F = B\bar{C} + \bar{A}BC + A\bar{B}\bar{C} + AC$. Show how you would implement your answer by using two NOR gates only. [A + B]

5 Three civilians (A, B, C) and an Army officer (D) are seated in a compartment on a train. The window will be open if the officer and at least *two* of the civilians vote to have it open.

(a) Write out a truth table for the window OPEN situation, taking a YES vote to equal 1 in the table and OPEN equal to 1.
(b) Use a K-map to minimise the logical equation for the situation.

[ABD + ACD + BCD]

6 Simplify $AD + A\bar{B}\bar{C} + \bar{B}C\bar{D} + \bar{A}CD + \bar{A}BC\bar{D}$ by using a Karnaugh mapping with sixteen cells. [$AD + A\bar{B} + \bar{A}C$]

7 Construct a truth table for the logic system shown in *Fig 14*. Use a K-map to simplify the logical equation derived from this truth table and check your result against the table.

[$\overline{\bar{A}CD}$]

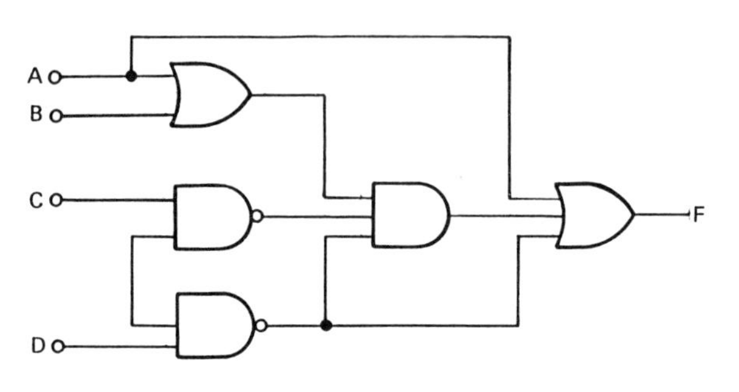

Fig 14

11 Sequential logic systems

A. MAIN POINTS CONCERNING SEQUENTIAL SYSTEMS

1 We come now to what are known as **sequential** logic systems in which the circuits, of which registers and counters are examples, work with timed sequences of clock pulses. This distinguishes these systems from the combinational circuits discussed earlier. There the gate outputs were determined by the inputs; in sequential systems the outputs may be affected by past inputs because information can be stored and released as required. The basic circuit unit for sequential logic systems is the bistable multivibrator or **flip-flop**. There are a number of varieties of the flip-flop and each has its own particular characteristics.

2 A flip-flop is a **two-state** element which can be set in either of the two states and remain in that state until some other input signal changes it. Basically, flip-flops store and release one bit of information in response to each input signal. A flip-flop circuit using discrete transistors is shown in *Fig 1*. As the circuit is symmetrical it might seem that both transistors would draw equal currents continuously, but this is impossible in a practical circuit. No circuit components or transistors can ever be precisely matched. Hence, at switch-on, one collector current is going to be greater than the other. Suppose the collector current of T_1 to be slightly greater than that of T_2 and increasing. The voltage drop across R_1 will increase and the collector potential will fall. This fall will be sensed at the base of T_2 via resistor R_3 and the collector current of T_2 will decrease. The consequent rise in the collector voltage of T_2 will be coupled back to the base of T_1 via resistor R_4, where it will augment the increase in collector current already taking place. The effect will be cumulative and the action will continue until T_1 is driven into saturation and T_2 is cut off. Nothing further can then happen without outside intervention. The whole action takes place in a fraction of a microsecond after switch-on. The circuit is now in one of its two possible **stable** states.

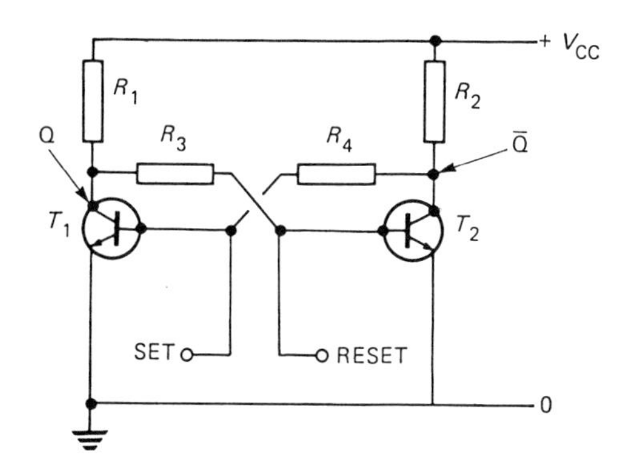

Fig 1

If we had started the above analysis by assuming that the collector current of T_2 was greater than that of T_1, and increasing, at switch-on, the regenerative action would have swung in the opposite direction, with T_2 being saturated and T_1 cut-off in the stable state. The two stable states are therefore, either T_1 is ON and T_2 is OFF, or conversely. So the outputs at the collectors are always complementary; if one of them is Q, the other is not-Q (or $\bar{Q}$). Because it has two stable states, this circuit is known as the bistable or, in digital applications, the R-S (RESET-SET) flip-flop.

3 Suppose that T_1 is switched ON and T_2 OFF in the circuit of *Fig 1*. If now a negative-going pulse is applied to the base of T_1 by way of the SET terminal, T_1 will be switched off and the circuit will change state in the manner already described. In this condition the circuit is again in a stable state and will remain so even when the trigger pulse ceases. The outputs Q and $\bar{Q}$ have, of course, interchanged. Any further negative pulses applied to the SET terminal will have no effect since T_1 is already switched off. However, a *negative* pulse applied to the RESET terminal will switch T_2 off and a change of state will immediately follow. The conventional way of representing this elementary flip-flop is shown in *Fig 2*.

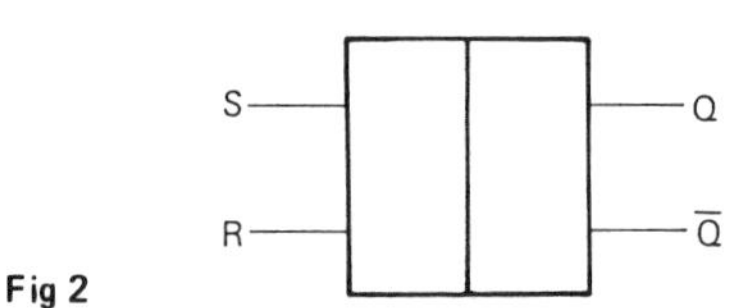

Fig 2

Triggering the R-S flip-flop in this way would not be very convenient in practice because it would be necessary to interchange the S and R inputs for each desired change of state. The difficulty can be overcome by modifying the circuit to that shown in *Fig 3*. Here the setting and resetting operation is carried out automatically, each negative pulse applied to the single input terminal causing a change of state.

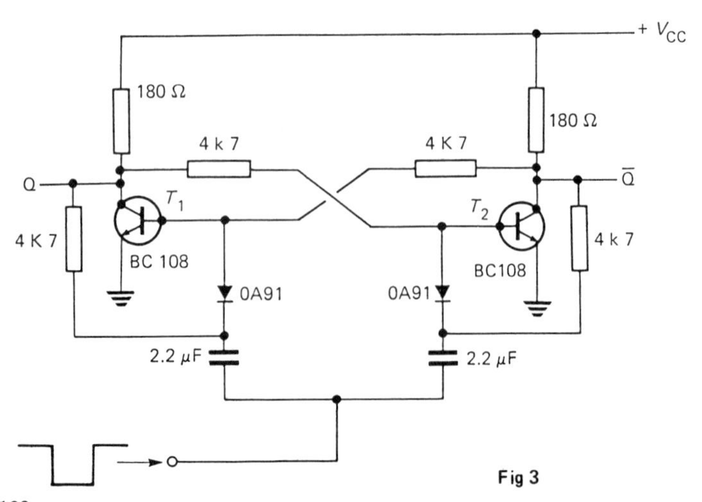

Fig 3

Two diodes have been added to the basic circuit and these direct or *steer* the input pulses to whichever transistor happens to be on and turns it off. *Fig 4* shows the wave-forms of the input and output signals for a succession of trigger pulses. Notice that the flip-flop changes state on the *falling* edge of the trigger pulses. If the output is taken from one collector only, there is *one* output pulse for every *two* input pulses. Thus the circuit functions as a binary divider. Any input frequency may be divided by any power of two (four, eight, sixteen, etc.) by combining the requisite number of flip-flops in cascade.

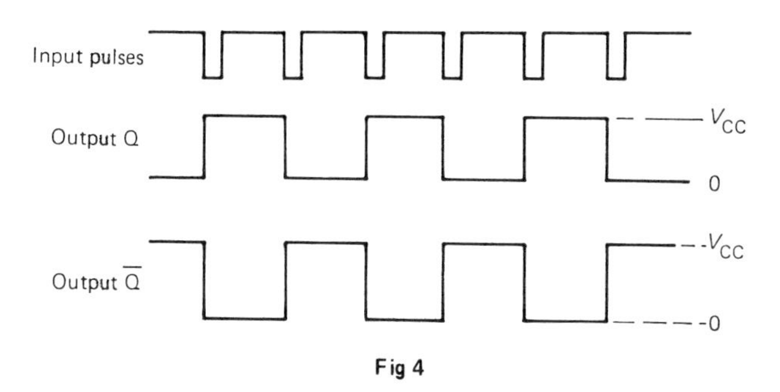

Fig 4

Make up the circuit of *Fig 3* for yourself; values have been indicated. A 6 V V_{CC} supply is suitable and the input can be standard 5 V square wave. Keep the frequency very low and if you use a 6 V, 60 mA bulb in place of one (or both) of the collector resistors, you will see the effect of the working of the bistable flip-flop.

4 Since each transistor stage in *Fig 1* is an inverter, this basic flip-flop is simply a pair of cross-coupled NOT gates, see *Fig 5*. If the gates are replaced by a pair of two-input NAND gates or a pair of two-input NOR gates, a controllable flip-flop becomes available which can be quickly assembled in integrated circuit form. *Fig 6* shows two NAND gates connected in this way.

The SET and RESET inputs connect to one of the inputs on each gate, the other inputs being connected to the opposite outputs in cross coupling. Suppose R and S both to be held at logic 1, then the NAND gates act simply as inverters and the system holds its output state indefinitely, that is, the outputs are 'stored' in whatever condition they were in already and the circuit is said to be **latched**. If S now falls to logic 0 whilst R remains at logic 1, output $\overline{Q}$ will switch to logic 1 because its NAND gate has an input at logic 0. In this condition the circuit is SET. Returning S and R to logic 1 will not reset the circuit and it will remain latched (or remember) with $\overline{Q} = 1$, $Q = 0$. In the same way, if R drops momentarily to logic 0 whilst S remains at 1,

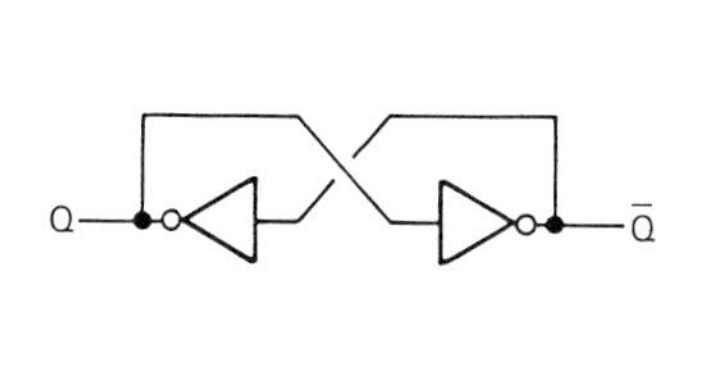

Fig 5

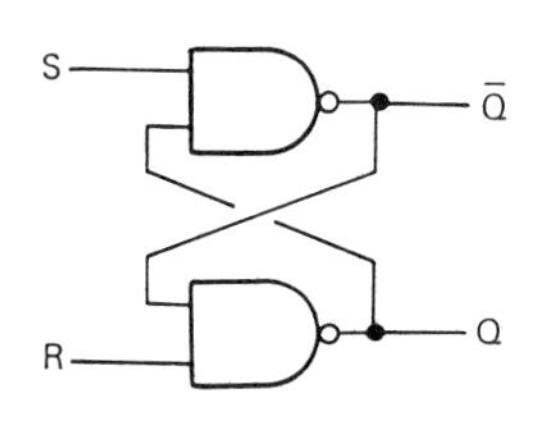

Fig 6

output $\bar{Q}$ will switch to logic 0 and hold there when R is returned to logic 1. The truth table for this R-S function is shown in *Fig 7*. You will notice that the output state is indeterminate when both S and R are at logic 0. This follows from the fact that *any* low input on a NAND gate makes the output high, hence for S = R = 0 both Q and $\bar{Q}$ would be high, which is impossible since the outputs must be complementary.

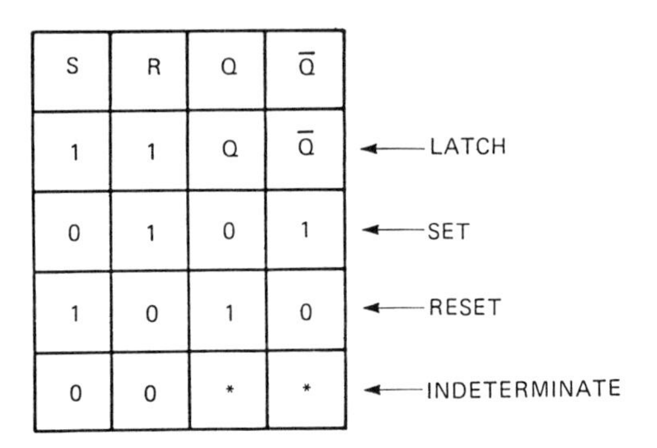

S	R	Q	$\bar{Q}$	
1	1	Q	$\bar{Q}$	← LATCH
0	1	0	1	← SET
1	0	1	0	← RESET
0	0	*	*	← INDETERMINATE

Fig 7

5 By adding additional circuitry to the R-S flip-flop just described it is given extra flexibility. *Fig 8* shows a modified circuit, the R-S flip-flop being preceded by two OR gates and a NOT gate. By this means, the facility of separate R and S inputs is retained while providing a common input terminal. If this input is fed with trigger pulses (or **clock** pulses), the input conditions are transferred to the output on one edge of the pulse.

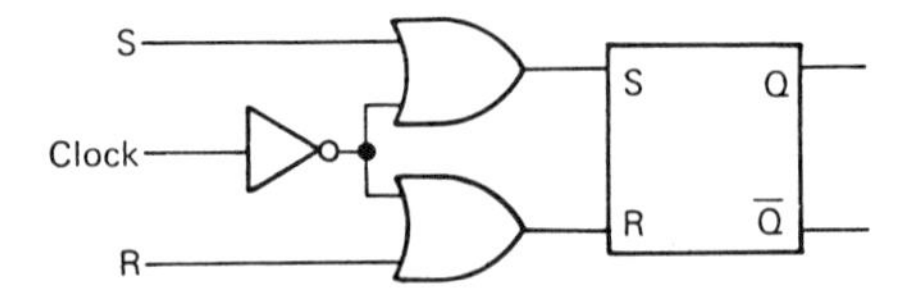

Fig 8

This circuit can only change state when the clock pulse is high. If the clock pulse is low, the output from the NOT gate is high, hence each OR gate has an input at logic 1 and their outputs must also be 1. Both inputs to the R-S flip-flop are therefore at 1 and, from the truth table, the Q and $\bar{Q}$ outputs are held. When the clock input goes high, however, the output from the NOT gate goes low and the OR gates each have an input at logic 0. The S and R on the flip-flop then depend only on the logic levels at the *external* S and R inputs, and in accordance with the truth table. This system is known as the **clocked R-S flip-flop**; it will respond to the R and S inputs only when the clock pulse is high. For this reason, this logic level is referred to as the **enabling** pulse.

6 The D (or data) flip-flop overcomes the problem of the basic R-S system which has an indeterminate state when both S and R inputs are at logic 0. An inverter is included between the R and S inputs as shown in *Fig 9*. When the clock input is high,

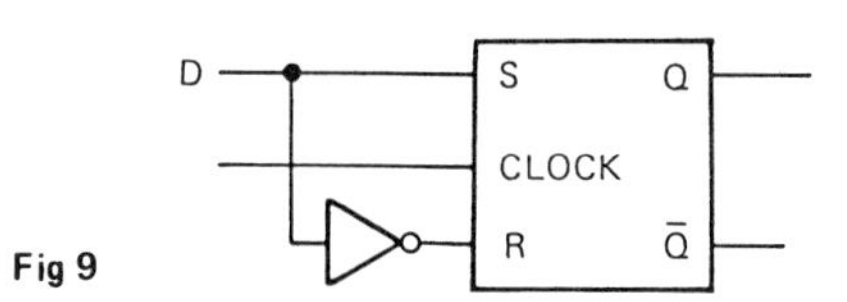

Fig 9

the Q output follows the D input. The logic state present on the D input just before the clock goes low will be latched on the output. One of the main uses for the D-latch is to hold a given binary number or a displayed output on a counter unit while the actual count sequence continues. The facility is often seen on the timing clocks used at sports meetings. The D-latch is available in integrated circuit form in the TTL series 7475 or the CMOS series 4042. For normal timing the clock input is held high by being connected to V_{CC}; for the latched condition it is connected low, connected to earth.

7 The J-K flip-flop is a further adaptation of flip-flop circuitry, being a combination of R-S and D-latch flip-flops. Additional control is provided by two extra input terminals, the preset and clear. This enables the flip-flop to be set up in a known state at switch on, so that the initial conditions are established prior to full operation. When not required, these inputs are held low and do not influence the normal operation of the circuit.

A circuit arrangement is shown in *Fig 10*. Two flip-flops are involved, one being the **master** and the other the **slave**. The master responds to data from the J and K inputs when the clock pulse is high, but this is *only* transferred to the output (slave) flip-flop as the clock goes low. The clock feeds directly to the master but by way of an inverter to the slave. The slave consequently receives a high clock input when the true clock is low and the Q output is waiting to respond to any change in the D input. Such a change cannot occur, however, all the time the clock is low because the master is in a stable state reached when the clock was last high.

When the clock does go high, the Q output of the master responds to the R and S inputs but the D input on the slave is unresponsive because the clock input is now low by way of the inverter. When the clock returns to low, the Q output of the master is held in the new state and, simultaneously, the slave clock input goes high and enables it to respond to this new state. Hence the J-K flip-flop changes its output state on the falling edge of the clock pulse, in that the master receives the information on the

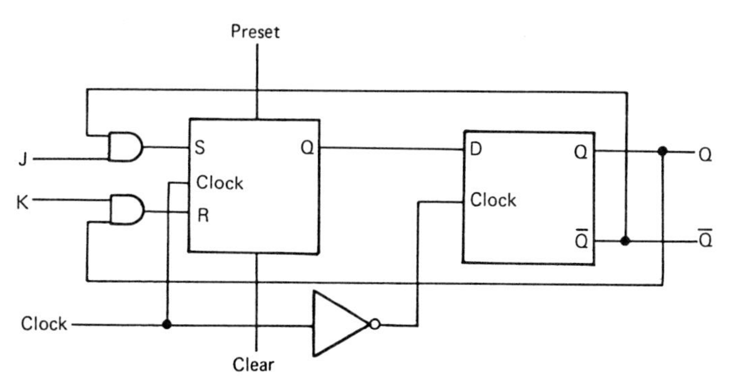

Fig 10

positive edge and transfers it to the slave on the falling edge. Since the clock does the triggering, the inputs themselves have no need to be in pulse form. To summarise: the operating sequence is that first the slave is isolated from the master, then the J and K inputs are entered into the master. These inputs are then disabled and finally the information is transferred from the master to the slave.

J-K flip-flops are available in integrated packages, the 7474 being a dual D-type latch and the 7476 a dual J-K flip-flop with preset and clear facilities. The preset input allows either a 1 or a 0 to be stored in the system; the clear input allows all old data to be cleared to 0, an example of which you will recognise in the Clear button of a pocket calculator.

B. WORKED PROBLEMS ON SEQUENTIAL SYSTEMS

Problem 1 *Fig 11* shows two NOR gates used in a basic R-S type flip-flop. Explain briefly how this circuit works.

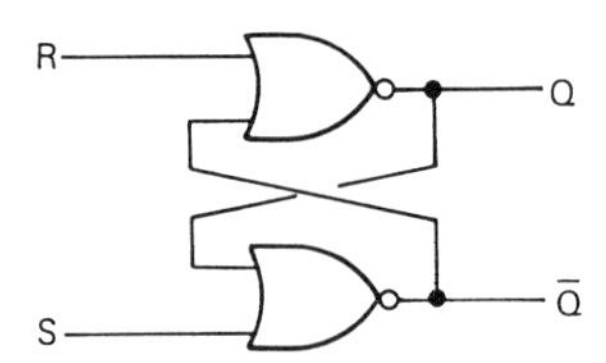

Fig 11

We described the two-NAND gate flip-flop earlier in the text. This is simply an alternative design. Remembering the rules for NOR gate operation, assume that the S input is high and the R input low. Also, assume that the Q output is high. If the S input goes low, the Q output will remain high. If, however, the R input goes high, output Q will go low. Only a change in the R input will cause this to happen.

In the same way, if we assume that output Q is low, only a change at the input to S from low to high will cause the circuit to change state (or flop back) so that Q will change from low to high. In the case of the two-NAND gate flip-flop, if both inputs were low, the output was indeterminate. Here, the output will be indeterminate if both inputs are simultaneously high.

Problem 2 Describe the three possible ways of triggering a flip-flop.

The three ways are known as (a) positive-edge triggered, (b) negative-edge triggered, (c) level-triggered.

In the positive-edge triggered flip-flop, the system responds to the leading edge of the clock signal. The information is therefore transferred from input to output as the clock pulse rises from low to high.

In the negative-edge triggered flip-flop, the system responds to the trailing edge of the clock signal, and the information is transferred as the clock pulse falls from high to low.

In the level-triggered flip-flop, the system responds not to *changes* in the state of the clock signal but to the actual logic state; triggering occurs, that is, when the clock is either high or low, but not when it is changing.

Problem 3 How can a series of interconnected flip-flops be used to store a binary number?

When a number of flip-flops are connected together to form a storage device for binary numbers, the system is known as a **shift register.** *Fig 12* shows four J-K flip-flops connected to form a 4-stage shift register. This system will store a 4-bit binary number from 0000 to 1111, or 0 to 15 in our ordinary denary system. To illustrate the action we will enter the binary number 1010 into the register. Firstly, all the flip-flops are reset to 0 by momentarily taking the clear input high. The number 1010 is then represented by the logic levels 1, 0, 1 and 0 and is fed one bit at a time into the J terminal of flip-flop A. The K terminal receives the complement of the J input by way of an inverter. At the first clock pulse, $J_A = 1$ and $K_A = 0$, so that Q_1 is set and the first digit is stored in the A flip-flop. At the second clock pulse, J_B is found to be 1 so B is reset and this logic level is transferred to output Q_2. At the same instant, flip-flop A now has a logical 0 on J_A (and 1 on K_A) so that Q_1 switches to 0 on this second clock pulse. Two of the digits are now stored in the register. After four such clock pulses, the full number 1010 is entered in the register. If LED indicators are connected to the Q output points, they will display the stored number by lighting where the output is high.

Shift registers are employed to store information for a great number of purposes: arithmetic calculations and operations, programme control, buffers in the movement of data, to name only three.

Problem 4 What is meant by the terms *serial* and *parallel* data transmission?

These terms can be best defined by considering the shift register covered in the previous problem. To reduce the number of connecting wires, digital data words are usually sent from one point to some other point in serial form; that is, the bits are sent one after another along a single wire. This was the method used in entering the number 1010 into the shift register. The output, however, is available at the Q outputs as simultaneously available digits; this is the parallel form of the data. Computers usually process their information in parallel form, but their inputs are in serial form, coming as a time sequence of 1s and 0s from the keyboard, magnetic tape or other source. *Fig 13* shows how two shift registers might be used to connect a keyboard to a data terminal over a single wire link. It would not be possible to send the bits in parallel form over such a link because each bit would require its own separate line. Hence it is necessary to convert any input to the link into a serial mode of transmission and reconvert it back to parallel mode at the output of the link. The system is kept in step (or synchronised) by using a common clock signal. In the figure the registers are used as parallel-in/serial-out (PISO) at the sending end and as serial-in/parallel-out (SIPO) at the receiving end. The integrated circuit type 74164 is an example of a SIPO converter.

Problem 5 How can a series of flip-flops be used as a simple counting system?

A counter is, basically, a serial register with a single input which receives the pulses to be counted in serial form and provides the summation in parallel form from each of the flip-flops making up the system. We have already noted earlier that a flip-flop is essentially

J input
K input
Clock
1
0
1
0
1
2
3
4
5
t

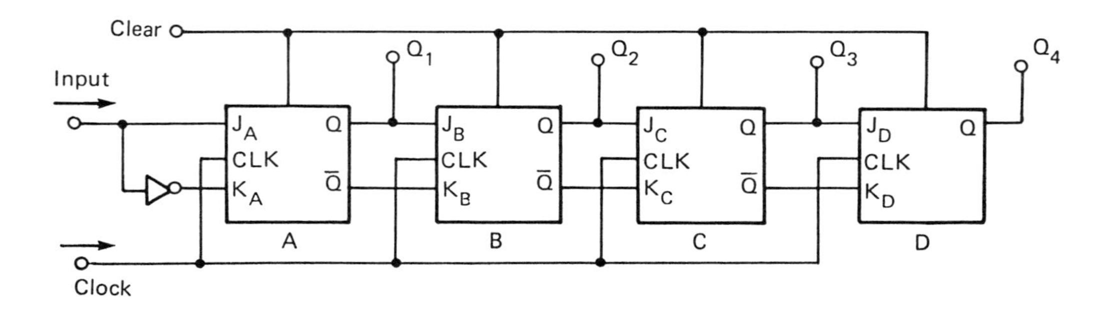
Clear
Input
Clock
Q_1
Q_2
Q_3
Q_4
J_A
CLK
K_A
Q
$\bar{Q}$
A
J_B
CLK
K_B
Q
$\bar{Q}$
B
J_C
CLK
K_C
Q
$\bar{Q}$
C
J_D
CLK
K_D
Q
D

Fig 12

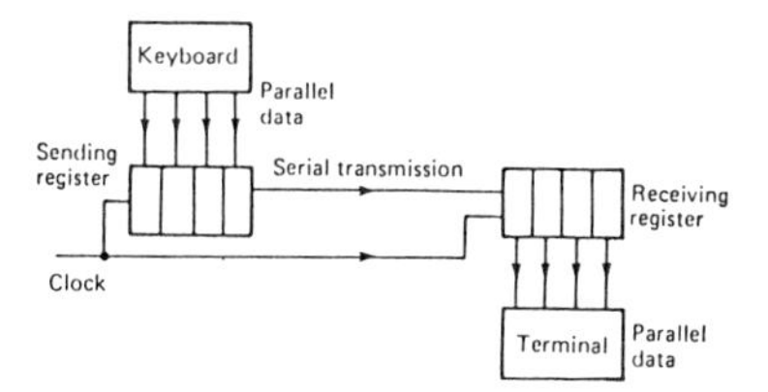

Fig 13

a divide-by-two device. *Fig 14* shows an assembly of four J-K flip-flops making up an elementary 4-bit binary counter. Counters of this sort are known as asynchronous because the counting sequence is not synchronised to or by anything else. As for the register, the outputs are cleared to zero by taking the clear input high. The pulse input is fed in at the CLOCK terminal of the first flip-flop. The count is available as a four digit binary number on the parallel Q_1 to Q_4 outputs. Notice that Q_4 is the least significant digit (LSD), that is, as we look at the diagram, the output number is 'backwards'. As each flip-flop divides the input by two, each time any output goes from 0 to 1, the following flip-flop switches over (or toggles) to the opposite state. It consequently takes two 1-to-0 transitions at the input to cause output Q_1 to change once; four transitions to cause output Q_2 to change once; eight transitions to cause Q_3 to change once; and sixteen transitions to cause Q_4 to change once. So, after each input pulse the circuit gives a binary representation of the number of pulses received up to that point. After the fifteenth pulse (1111) the stages reset to zero and the count begins again. This is a scale-of-sixteen counter. If numbers greater than 1111 (decimal 15) have to be counted, more stages must be added. N stages will give a scale of 2^N counter.

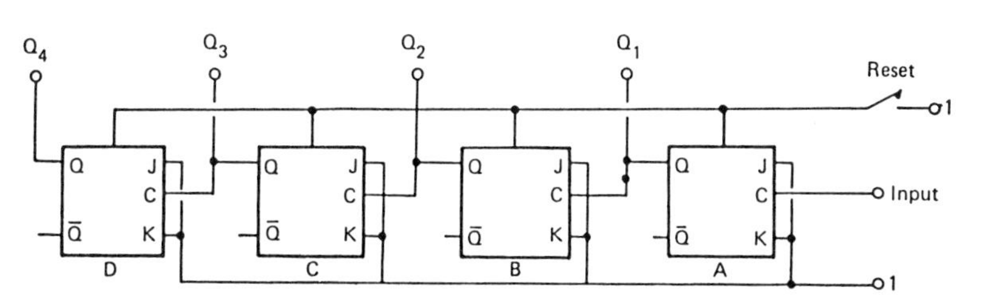

Fig 14

Problem 6 How could the scale-of-sixteen be modified to operate as a scale-of-ten counter?

Counting in the decimal or modulo-10 system is more convenient than any other because the binary coded outputs from the flip-flop stages can then be fed to suitable decoders and displayed in a readable form, as for example, in a pocket calculator. A modification of the basic counter system is shown in *Fig 15*. For clarity, the J and K inputs are omitted. The binary equivalent of decimal 10 is 1010; this has four digits and can be handled by a four-input logic gate. Several alternatives are possible but in this example an AND gate is used. Notice that the four inputs to this gate are taken from the Q outputs on the A and C flip-flops and from the $\overline{Q}$ outputs on the B and D flip-flops.

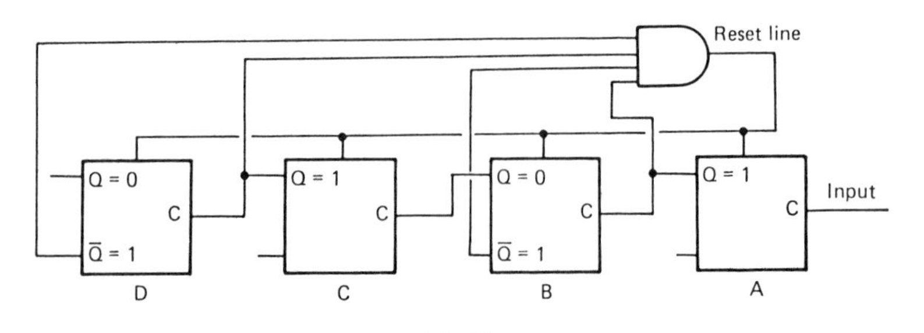

Fig 15

When the count reaches 1010 at the four Q terminals respectively, the inputs to the AND gate will all be simultaneously at logic 1, and the output from the AND will then also be 1. This output applied to all four reset (CLEAR) inputs on the flip-flops will cause the counter to reset to 0000 on the count of ten, after which the cycle will recommence.

Problem 7 How could *Fig 15* be modified to make a scale-of-twelve counter?

All that is required is a change to the AND gate inputs, noting that A is the *most* significant digit. The binary equivalent of decimal 12 is 1100, hence by taking the Q outputs from flip-flops A and B, and the $\overline{Q}$ outputs from flip-flops C and D, the counter will reset on the count of 12 (or 1100).

Integrated circuits 7490 and 7493 are examples of counter systems, each containing four J-K flip-flops and reset facilities. Division by two, three, five, eight and ten is easily arranged.

C. FURTHER PROBLEMS ON SEQUENTIAL SYSTEMS

(a) SHORT ANSWER PROBLEMS (answers on page 134)

1. Explain what is meant by the term sequential circuits.
2. What is a flip-flop? What is its basic function?
3. Explain the operation and draw the truth table for a flip-flop consisting of two NOR gates.
4. What keeps the outputs of an R-S flip-flop from switching when one input changes to 0 while the other is held at 0?
5. Explain the difference between serial and parallel data transmission.
6. Which kind of register can convert data from serial to parallel form?
7. What happens at the output of an R-S flip-flop if output Q is 0, both inputs R and S are 0, when a momentary 1 pulse is applied at S?
8. Why is it possible to use a chain of J-K flip-flops as a counter system?

(b) CONVENTIONAL PROBLEMS

1. How many J-K flip-flops are needed to count up to decimal 128? [7]
2. Two J-K flip-flops are connected as shown in *Fig 16*. If the flip-flops respond to falling edge transitions, what will the output be if the input is a 1 kHz square wave? [250 Hz]

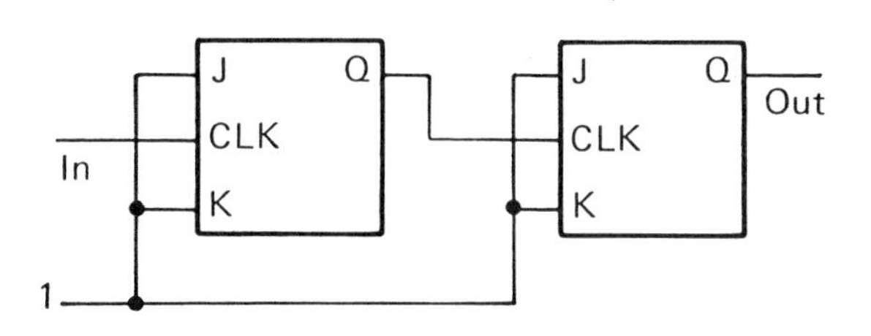

Fig 16

3 What is the final output frequency of an 8-stage binary divider having an input of 10 240 Hz? [40 Hz]

4 Draw a block diagram of a binary counter that will count up to 100.

5 With the aid of a diagram for each, explain the operation of (a) a 4-bit shift register, (b) a 4-bit counter.

6 *Fig 17* shows a hypothetical integrated circuit package containing three identical gates. By using all these gates, how would you connect the numbered pins together so that the whole system represented an OR gate? The output is to come from pin 8.

7 Explain carefully with diagrams, what purpose the master-slave principle serves in a flip-flop.

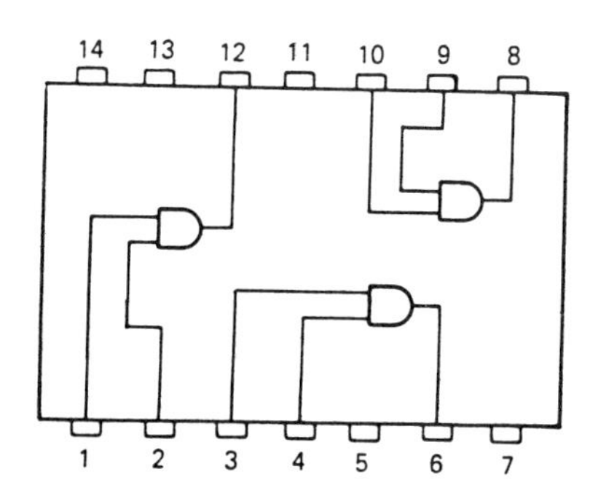

Fig 17

Answers to problems

CHAPTER 1

1 Hydrogen
2 11
3 *n*-type
4 The table should be as follows:

	Protons	*K*	*L*	*M*	*N*	*shells*
Aluminium	13	2	8	3	0	
Argon	18	2	8	8	0	
Copper	29	2	8	18	1	
Magnesium	12	2	8	2	0	

5 (a) protons, neutrons; (b) equal; (c) hole-electron pairs, thermal; (d) acceptor; (e) extrinsic, (f) descrease, increase.
6 (a) F; (b) T; (c) T; (d) F; (e) F; (f) T; (g) T; (h) T; (j) T.

CHAPTER 2

2 (a) natural, (b) charge; (c) anode; (d) electrons, impurity, holes; (e) same; (f) silicon germanium; (g) zero, infinite; (h) zero.
3 (a) F; (b) T; (c) T; (d) T; (e) T; (f) T; (g) F.
4 40 μA.

Multi-choice problems:

1 (a); 2 (b); 3 (b), 4 (c); 5 (c), 6 (b).

CHAPTER 3

2 (a) zero; infinite; (b) infinite; (c) four; (d) one-third; (e) doubles.
4 No; the peak applied voltage is 340 V.
5 (a) 50 V; (b) 25 V.
6 (a) current reduced; (b) rectification would cease.
7 (a) F; (b) T; (c) F; (d) T; (e) T; (f) T.

Multi-choice problems:

1 (b); 2 (c); 3 (c); 4 (a); 5 (c); 6 (b); 7 (b); 8 (a).

CHAPTER 4

1 (a) forward, reverse; (b) positive; (c) towards; (d) base, collector; (e) I_c; (f) common-emitter, (g) electrons; (h) into; (j) unit.
2 0.024 mA.
3 (i) 0.9875; (ii) 79.
4 0.995.
5 67.5.
6 (a) F; (b) T; (c) F, (d) T; (e) F; (f) T; (g) T; (h) T; (j) F; (k) T; (l) T.

CHAPTER 5

1 (a) F, (b) T; (c) F; (d) T; (e) T; (f) T; (g) T; (h) F (V_{BE} decreases). (j) T; (k) F.
2 (a) increase; (b) decrease; (c) transistor; (d) negative; (e) R_L; (f) V_{CC}; (g) unity; (h) centre.
3 1750.
4 −1/5000 siemen.
5 (a) 90 k; (b) 84 k.
6 3 V.

Multi-choice problems:

1 (i) (a); (ii) (b); (iii) (b); (iv) (b); (v) (b)
2 (i) (b); (ii) (c); (iii) (b); (iv) (a); (v) (b)

CHAPTER 6

Multi-choice problems:

1(c); 2(c); 3(b); 4(d); 5(b); 6(b); 7(b); 8(a).

CHAPTER 7

Multi-choice problems:

1(a); 2(c); 3(c); 4(a); 5(b); 6(c); 7(a); 8(d).

CHAPTER 8

1 Series switches; 2 Parallel switches; 3 NOT gate; 4 Four;
5 AB + AC + AD + AE = A(B + C + D + E).
6 (a) OR; (b) NOT; (c) A.B; (d) OR; (e) $\overline{A}$; (f) B; (g) exclusive OR.

Multi-choice problems:

1 (a); 2 (b); 3 (a); 4 (c), 5 (c); 6 (b); 7 (a); 8 (c).

CHAPTER 9

1 (a) AND; (b); 1; (c) inverse or negation; (d) diodes, transistors; (e) AND, NOT; (f) OR, NOT; (g) NOT; (h) 1; (j) OR.
2 (a) (iii); (b) (iii); (c) (i); (d) (iv); (e) (i).
3 AND gate.
4 100101001
5 1000001
6 110100

CHAPTER 10

1 16.
2 Yes.
3 A product form such as ABC.
5 Yes.
6 (a) and (b).
7 Only the lower right cell contains a 1.

CHAPTER 11

3 See *Fig 7* of Chapter 11 and reverse the S and R columns, top to bottom.
4 The output of each gate is fed back to another input on the other gate.
6 SIPO shift register.
7 Q goes from 0 to 1.
8 They count in binary which can be converted to decimal for readout purposes.

Index